ENERGY EFFICIENCY

ENERGY EFFICIENCY

LARA S. ZAMBINI
EDITOR

Novinka Books
New York

NOTICE TO THE READER

The Publisher has taken reasonable care in the preparation of this book, but makes no expressed or implied warranty of any kind and assumes no responsibility for any errors or omissions. No liability is assumed for incidental or consequential damages in connection with or arising out of information contained in this book. The Publisher shall not be liable for any special, consequential, or exemplary damages resulting, in whole or in part, from the readers' use of, or reliance upon, this material.

This publication is designed to provide accurate and authoritative information with regard to the subject matter covered herein. It is sold with the clear understanding that the Publisher is not engaged in rendering legal or any other professional services. If legal or any other expert assistance is required, the services of a competent person should be sought. FROM A DECLARATION OF PARTICIPANTS JOINTLY ADOPTED BY A COMMITTEE OF THE AMERICAN BAR ASSOCIATION AND A COMMITTEE OF PUBLISHERS.

LIBRARY OF CONGRESS CATALOGING-IN-PUBLICATION DATA
Available upon request

ISBN 1-59454-684-3

Published by Nova Science Publishers, Inc. ✤ *New York*

CONTENTS

PREFACE

Energy efficiency sounds good but so far the steps to reach it have been baby steps. This book deals with commercial and consumer product efficiency standards, new goals for energy efficiency and renewable energy in federal facilities and fleets, the Energy Star products program, reforming hydropower relicensing, expanding programs for hydrogen fuel cell buses, and setting a renewable fuels standard for increased use of ethanol and biodiesel. Energy facts are given and policy is discussed.

Chapter 1 reviews the status of energy efficiency and renewable energy legislation introduced during the 109th Congress. Action in the first session has focused on the omnibus energy policy bills H.R. 6 and S. 10 (Energy Policy Act of 2005). H.R. 6 contains many, if not most, of the energy efficiency and renewable energy provisions in the conference report on H.R. 6 from the 108th Congress. One key exception is the absence of a proposal to extend the renewable energy production tax credit (PTC), which is due to expire at the end of 2005.

Energy security, a major driver of federal energy efficiency programs in the past, came back into play as oil and gas prices rose late in the year 2000. The terrorist attack in 2001 and the Iraq war have led to heightened concern for energy security and raised further concerns about the vulnerability of energy infrastructure and the need for alternative fuels. Further, the 2001 power shortages in California, the 2003 northeast-midwest power blackout, and continuing high natural gas and oil prices have brought a renewed emphasis on energy efficiency and energy conservation to dampen electricity, oil, and natural gas demand. Also, worldwide emphasis on environmental problems of air and water pollution and global climate change, the related development of clean energy technologies in western Europe and Japan, and technology competitiveness may remain important influences on energy efficiency policymaking. As reported in chapter 2, the Bush Administration's FY2006 budget request for the Department of Energy's (DOE's) Energy Efficiency Program seeks $846.8 million, $21.4 million less than FY2005. This includes $575.8 million for R&D and $271.0 million for grants.

Energy supplies and prices are a major economic factor in the United States, and energy markets are volatile and unpredictable. For both these reasons, energy policy is of frequent interest to the Congress. Chapter 3 presents a statistical view of the supply and consumption of various forms of energy. After an introductory overview of aggregate energy consumption, the report presents detailed analysis of trends and statistics regarding specific energy sources: oil, electricity, natural gas, and coal. A section on trends in energy efficiency is also presented.

Historically, U.S. federal energy tax policy promoted the supply of oil and gas. However, the 1970s witnessed (1) a significant cutback in the oil and gas industry's tax preferences, (2) the imposition of new excise taxes on oil, and (3) the introduction of numerous tax preferences for energy conservation, the development of alternative fuels, and the commercialization of the technologies for producing these fuels (renewables such as solar, wind, and biomass, and non-conventional fossil fuels such as shale oil and coalbed methane). The Reagan Administration, using a free-market approach, advocated repeal of the windfall profit tax on oil and the repeal or phase-out of most energy tax preferences —for oil and gas, as well as alternative fuels. Due to the combined effects of the Economic Recovery Tax Act and the energy tax subsidies that had not been repealed, which together created negative effective tax rates in some cases, the actual energy tax policy differed from the stated policy. The George H. W. Bush and Bill Clinton years witnessed a return to a much more activist energy tax policy, with an emphasis on energy conservation and alternative fuels. While the original aim was to reduce demand for imported oil, energy tax policy was also increasingly viewed as a tool for achieving environmental and fiscal objectives as reported in chapter 4.

In: Energy Efficiency
Editor: Lara S. Zambini, pp. 1-40
ISBN: 1-59454-684-3
© 2006 Nova Science Publishers, Inc.

Chapter 1

ENERGY EFFICIENCY AND RENEWABLE ENERGY LEGISLATION IN THE 109TH CONGRESS*

Fred Sissine

SUMMARY

This article reviews the status of energy efficiency and renewable energy legislation introduced during the 109th Congress. Action in the first session has focused on the omnibus energy policy bills H.R. 6 and S. 10 (Energy Policy Act of 2005). H.R. 6 contains many, if not most, of the energy efficiency and renewable energy provisions in the conference report on H.R. 6 from the 108th Congress. One key exception is the absence of a proposal to extend the renewable energy production tax credit (PTC), which is due to expire at the end of 2005.

H.R. 6 would authorize or reauthorize most energy efficiency and renewable energy programs. It also would establish several new commercial and consumer product efficiency standards, set new goals for energy efficiency and renewable energy in federal facilities and fleets, expand the Energy Star products program, reform hydropower relicensing, expand programs for hydrogen fuel cell buses, and set a renewable fuels standard for increased use of ethanol and biodiesel.

---

* Excerpted from CRS Report RL32860 dated June 10, 2005.

The Senate Committee on Energy and Natural Resources reported S. 10 on June 9, 2005. The bill contains many of the same non-tax energy efficiency and renewable energy provisions that are in H.R. 6. One notable difference is that S. 10 does not have the daylight savings provision that appears in H.R. 6. Also, S. 10 has a renewable fuel standard (RFS) of 8 billion gallons, which contrasts with the provision for 5 billion gallons in H.R. 6. In further contrast to the House bill, S. 10 has a greater number of legislated (instead of rulemaking-specified) energy efficiency standards for consumer products and commercial equipment. Additionally, S. 10 has a provision that calls for saving one million barrels of oil per day.

Other action in the first session has focused on H.R. 3 (Transportation Equity Act), which has some provisions on clean (renewable) fuels, energy conservation, and advanced vehicle technologies.

More than 100 energy efficiency and renewable energy bills have been introduced thus far, covering a broad range of policy and issue areas. So far, more of these bills have focused on tax incentives than any other policy area. The bills also cover a wide range of sectors that include buildings, defense, education, federal lands/energy management, farms, American Indians, and international activities. The bills are also categorized by type of renewable resource, type of energy efficiency measure, and technology.

For each bill listed in this article, a brief description and a summary of action are given, including references to committee hearings and reports. Also, a selected list of hearings on renewable energy is included.

INTRODUCTION

This report summarizes action on more than 100 energy efficiency and renewable energy bills introduced during the 109th Congress.[1] These bills cover a wide range of policy and issue areas that include appropriations, authorizations, research and development, grants, loans, financing, regulation (including a renewable portfolio standard), tax credits, funding, goals, plans, impacts, and the environment/climate change. So far, most of these bills have focused on tax credits and incentives. The bills also cover a range of sectors that include buildings, defense, education, federal lands/energy management, farms, American Indians, and international

---

[1] This report is intended to complement and support CRS Issue Brief IB10020 Energy Efficiency: Budget, Oil Conservation, and Electricity Conservation Issues and CRS Issue Brief IB10041 Renewable Energy: Tax Credit, Budget, and Electricity Production Issues.

activities. Thus far, the sector of federal lands/energy management has generated the greatest number of bills. **Table 2** groups the bills by topic. The bills are also categorized by type of renewable resource, type of energy efficiency measure, and technology. There is a broad range of efficiency measures and technologies, including cogeneration (combined heat and power), distributed generation, net metering, equipment and appliance standards, fuel economy standards, and transportation efficiency. The bills are fairly evenly distributed among these areas. There is also a broad range of renewable energy resources and technologies, including alcohol fuels, biofuels, biodiesel, biopower, biomass, geothermal, hydrogen, hydropower, solar, and wind. So far, the areas of fuels and wind energy have generated the greatest number of bills.

In the first session, action has focused on the omnibus energy policy bills H.R. 6 and S. 10 (Energy Policy Act of 2005). H.R. 6 passed the House on April 21, 2005. It comprises H.R. 1541 (tax provisions), H.R. 1640 (non-tax provisions), and the Resources Committee print "Domestic Energy Security Act" (non-tax provisions). The energy efficiency and renewable energy provisions of H.R. 6 contain many, if not most, of the energy efficiency and renewable energy recommendations in the conference report on H.R. 6 from the 108th Congress. One notable exception is the absence of a proposal to extend the renewable energy production tax credit (PTC), which is due to expire at the end of 2005.[2]

The Senate Committee on Energy and Natural Resources reported S. 10 on June 9, 2005. The bill contains many of the same non-tax energy efficiency and renewable energy provisions that are in H.R. 6. One notable difference is that S. 10 does not have the daylight savings provision that appears in H.R. 6. Also, S. 10 has a renewable fuel standard (RFS) of 8 billion gallons, which contrasts with the provision for 5 billion gallons in H.R. 6. In further contrast to the House bill, S. 10 has a greater number of legislated (instead of rulemaking-specified) energy efficiency standards for consumer products and commercial equipment. Additionally, S. 10 has a provision that calls for saving one million barrels of oil per day.

H.R. 6 contains provisions that would authorize or reauthorize several energy efficiency and renewable energy programs. It also would establish several new commercial and consumer product efficiency standards, set new goals for energy efficiency and renewable energy in federal facilities and fleets, expand the Energy Star products program, reform hydropower

---

[2] The PTC was extended through the end of 2005 by P.L. 108-311 (§313) and by P.L. 108-357 (§710). Section 1302 of the conference report (H.Rept. 108-375)on H.R. 6 in the 108th Congress proposed a PTC extension.

relicensing, expand programs for hydrogen fuel cell buses, and set a renewable fuels standard for increased use of ethanol and biodiesel.

Other action in the first session has focused on the Transportation Equity Act (H.R. 3), which has some provisions on clean (renewable) fuels, energy conservation, and advanced vehicle technologies. Action on these bills is summarized in **Table 1**.

Table 1. Action on Energy Efficiency and Renewable Energy Legislation, 109th Congress

Bill	Category	Action	Date
H.R. 3	Transportation equity bill	Passed Senate	5/17/2005
		Passed House	3/10/2005
H.R. 6	Omnibus energy bill	Passed House, amended	4/21/2005
H.R. 610	Energy R&D authorization bill	Reported	2/10/2005
H.R. 1158	Steel and aluminum energy conservation reauthorization bill	Reported	3/17/2005
H.R. 2419	Appropriations (energy & water)	Passed House, amended	5/24/2005
S. 10	Omnibus energy bill (non-tax)	Reported	6/9/2005
S. 131	Clear Skies (clean air act) bill	Failed to pass committee	3/9/2005
S. 606	Renewable fuel standard	Ordered to be Reported	3/16/2005

For each bill listed in this report, a brief description and a summary of action are given, including references to committee hearings and reports. Also, a selected list of hearings on energy efficiency and renewable energy is included.

Table 2. Energy Efficiency and Renewable Energy Bills by Topic, 109th Congress

I. Policy and Issue Areas

Appropriations. H.R. 2419
Authorizations/Omnibus Energy Policy. *H.R. 6*, H.R. 610, H.R. 612, H.R. 1158, H.R. 1541, H.R. 1640, H.R. 2828, S. 10, S. 665, S. 726
Research and Development. H.R. 610, H.R. 612, S. 387
Grants. H.R. 3/S. 732, H.R. 168, H.R. 610, H.R. 722, H.R. 1215
Loans/Financing. H.R. 388, S. 269, S. 426
Renewable Portfolio Standard. H.R. 983, H.R. 2828, S. 427
Tax Incentive for Investment. H.R. 17, H.R. 206, H.R. 424, H.R. 626, H.R. 1212, H.R. 1397/S. 671, H.R. 1541, H.R. 2070, H.R. 2794, S. 387, S. 680/H.R. 1834, S. 715, S. 962, S. 971
Tax Incentive for Energy Production. H.R. 36/S. 610, H.R. 141, H.R. 381, S. 35, S. 387, S. 542, S. 1078, S. 1079, S. 1093, S. 1156
Tax Incentive for Fuel Use. H.R. 113, H.R. 206, H.R. 1255, H.R. 2498/S. 1076, S. 1077
Goals/Plans/Impact Information. H.R. 3/S. 732, H.R. 373, H.R. 610, H.R. 722, H.R. 1158, S. 606
Environment/Climate Change. H.R. 759, H.R. 1451, S. 386, S. 387, S. 388, S. 745, S. 883, S. 887, S. 1151, S. 1203

II. Sectors

Buildings. H.R. 610, H.R. 612, H.R. 722, H.R. 737, H.R. 1212, H.R. 2751, S. 680/H.R. 1834
Defense. H.R. 174, H.R. 1815/S. 1042
Education. H.R. 737, S. 726
Federal Lands/Energy Management. H.R. 174, H.R. 705, H.R. 722, H.R. 779, H.R. 983, H.R. 1533, H.R. 1750, S. 650/H.R. 1608, S. 665, S. 680/H.R. 1834, S. 890, S. 1208
Farms/American Indians. H.R. 622/S. 326, S. 269, S. 373, S. 502, S. 542
International/Trade. H.R. 1212, S. 388, S. 745, S. 680/H.R. 1834

Table 2. Continued

III. Energy Efficiency Measures and Technologies

Cogeneration/Combined Heat and Power (CHP). S. 386, S. 388, S. 726
Distributed Generation/Net Metering/Electric Power. S. 150, S. 426, S. 726
Equipment/Lighting/Appliances. H.R. 737, H.R. 1421, S. 426, S. 726, S. 680/H.R. 1834, S. 1022
Fuel Economy. H.R. 705/S. 889, H.R. 722, H.R. 1103/S. 836, H.R. 2070, H.R. 2665, S. 889/H.R. 705
Transportation. H.R. 423, H.R. 444, H.R. 626, H.R. 722, H.R. 1705, H.R. 1706, H.R. 1744, H.R. 2070, H.R. 2358, S. 373, S. 808, S. 918

IV. Renewable Energy Resources and Technologies

Alcohol Fuels/Biofuels/Biodiesel. H.R. 3/S. 732, H.R. 36/S. 610, H.R. 113, H.R. 140, H.R 206, H.R. 325, H.R. 381, H.R. 388, H.R. 1255, H.R. 1398, H.R. 1608, H.R. 1612, H.R. 1744, S. 129, S. 373, S. 502, S. 587, S. 610, S. 650, S. 918
Biopower/Biomass. H.R. 610, H.R. 612, H.R. 622, H.R. 737, H.R. 983, H.R. 1127, H.R. 2498/S. 1076, S. 150, S. 326, S. 427, S. 502, S. 542, S. 1078, S. 1079, S. 1156, S. 1210
Geothermal. H.R. 174, H.R. 622/S. 326, H.R. 1127, S. 269
Hydrogen. H.R. 3/S. 732, H.R. 325, H.R. 610, H.R. 612, H.R. 626, H.R. 722, H.R. 737, H.R. 1750, S. 129, S. 373, S. 427, S. 436, S. 665, S. 726
Hydropower. H.R. 722, H.R. 737, H.R. 779, H.R. 971, H.R. 1530, S. 244, S. 427
Solar. H.R. 17, H.R. 381, H.R. 610, H.R. 612, H.R. 622/S. 326, H.R. 722, H.R. 737, H.R. 1127, S. 150, S. 269, S. 326, S. 426, S. 427, S. 726
Wind. H.R. 141, H.R. 381, H.R. 610, H.R. 612, H.R. 622/S. 326, H.R. 737, H.R. 759, H.R. 983, H.R. 1127, H.R. 1541, S. 35, S. 150, S. 269, S. 326, S. 342, S. 426, S. 427, S. 502, S. 542, S. 715, S. 1208

LEGISLATION

House Bills (with Senate Companions)

H.R. 3 (Young)/S. 732 (Inhofe)

Transportation Equity Act. Section 1208 on High-Occupancy Vehicle (HOV) Lanes includes provisions for alternative-fueled vehicles and energy-efficient vehicles. Section 3009 on Clean Fuels Formula Grant Program includes provisions for biodiesel, alcohol fuels, and fuel cells. Section 5213 on Metropolitan Planning directs that goals include energy conservation. Other provisions in the bill address traffic congestion, intelligent transportation systems, bicycling and pedestrian issues, and advanced vehicle technologies. House bill introduced February 9, 2005; referred to Committee on Transportation and Infrastructure. Reported (H.Rept. 109-12, Parts I and II) March 8. Passed House, amended, March 10. Senate bill reported (S.Rept. 109-53) April 6. In lieu of S. 732, Senate passed its version of H.R. 3, amended, May 17. House and Senate conferees appointed May 26.

H.R. 6 (Barton)

Energy Policy Act of 2005. Section 102 sets a goal for 20% energy reduction in federal facilities by 2015. Section 104 requires federal agency purchases of EPA Energy Star and FEMP-designated products. Section 105 permanently extends ESPCs and sets $500 million cap. Section 124 authorizes funding to states for rebates to support the cost premium for residential purchases of Energy Star products. Section 133 establishes energy efficiency standards for a variety of consumer products and commercial equipment. Title I also sets out several energy efficiency provisions for public housing. Title VII has provisions for hybrid, fuel cell, and electric vehicles; and revises and extends some aspects of fuel economy standards. Title IX reauthorizes DOE energy efficiency R&D programs. Section 1253 would, under certain conditions, terminate PURPA cogeneration requirements. Sections 1312 and 1317 would create $397 million in tax credits for energy efficiency. For renewables, reauthorizes REPI, authorizes increased hydropower at existing dams, sets renewables goal for federal facilities, and establishes residential rebate program. Also, Section 1311 provides $18 million in residential investment tax credits over three years for solar hot water, photovoltaics, and fuel cell equipment. Committee on Energy and Commerce ordered committee print reported, as amended, April 13. Incorporates H.R. 1640 (non-tax provisions), Domestic Energy Security Act, and H.R. 1541 (as Title XIII). Referred to Committees on Energy and

Commerce, Resources, Ways and Means, Science, and others April 18. Passed House, amended, April 21. H.Amdt. 74, as amended by H.Amdt. 75, directs EPA to revise certain adjustment factors used in federal vehicle fuel economy ratings and labels put on new vehicles. H.Amdt. 78 authorizes $20 million for installation of a photovoltaic solar electric system at DOE headquarters.

H.R. 17 (Hayworth)

Residential Solar Energy Tax Credit Act. Creates a 15% investment tax credit for photovoltaic (electric) equipment, with a maximum of $2,000. Also, it establishes a 15% credit for solar water heating equipment, with a maximum of $2,000. Introduced January 4, 2005; referred to Committee on Ways and Means.

H.R. 36 (S. King)/S. 610 (Talent)

Amends the Internal Revenue Code to revise the tax credit for biodiesel used as fuel to include a credit for the production of agri-biodiesel fuel equal to 10 cents for each gallon produced. Limits (1) the amount of qualified agri-biodiesel production of a producer to 15 million gallons for any taxable year; and (2) eligible producers to those with an annual productive capacity not exceeding 60 million gallons. Revises the small ethanol producer tax credit to (1) expand the eligibility of small ethanol producers for the credit; (2) exclude the credit from the definition of passive activity credit; and (3) exclude credit amounts from inclusion in gross income. House bill introduced January 4, 2005; referred to Committee on Ways and Means. Senate bill introduced March 11, 2005; referred to Committee on Finance.

H.R. 113 (M. Kennedy)

Requires the Secretary of Transportation to determine apportionments to states of federal-aid highway funds for FY2006 or any subsequent fiscal year in a particular manner if FY2005 or any preceding fiscal year is taken into account in the computation. Directs the Secretary, in such an instance, to base his calculations on the amount of estimated tax receipts that would have resulted if certain alcohol fuel mixture and biodiesel mixture excise tax credits under the American Jobs Creation Act of 2004 had taken effect at the beginning of the fiscal year. Introduced January 5, 2005; referred to Committee on Transportation and Infrastructure.

H.R. 140 (McHugh)

Promotes the use of anaerobic (methane) digesters by agricultural producers and rural small businesses to produce renewable energy and improve environmental quality. Introduced January 4, 2005; referred to Committee on Agriculture.

H.R. 141 (McHugh)

Makes permanent the renewable energy production tax credit (PTC) for producing electricity from wind. Introduced January 4, 2005; referred to Committee on Ways and Means.

H.R. 168 (Millender-McDonald)

Goods Movement Act of 2005. Directs the Secretary of Transportation to consider congestion relief, energy consumption, and intelligent transportation systems in selecting projects for grants to state and local government. Introduced January 4, 2005; referred to Committee on Transportation and Infrastructure.

H.R. 174 (Millender-McDonald)

Geothermal Energy Initiative Act of 2005. Calls for a new resource assessment, more access to federal land, improved leasing and permitting, and reimbursement for required environmental analyses. Introduced January 4, 2005; referred to Committee on Resources and the Committee on Agriculture.

H.R. 206 (Serrano)

Amends the Internal Revenue Code to allow certain businesses located in areas designated as nonattainment areas under the Clean Air Act a general business tax credit for the cost of certain clean-fuel vehicle property and clean-burning fuel. Allows the credit to be taken against regular and alternative minimum tax liabilities. Allows a tax deduction for any unused clean fuel credit amounts. The maximum credit is $2,000 for vehicles weighing less than 5 tons, $5,000 for vehicles weighing between 5 and 13 tons, and $50,000 for trucks and vans weighing more than 13 tons and for buses with 20 or more passengers. Introduced January 4, 2005; referred to Committee on Ways and Means.

H.R. 325 (Graves)/S. 129 (Talent)

Hybrid HOV Access Act. Allows energy-efficient and low-emission vehicles to use HOV facilities. House bill introduced January 25, 2005;

referred to Committee on Transportation and Infrastructure. Senate bill introduced January 24, 2005; referred to Committee on Environment and Public Works.

H.R. 381 (Gillmor)

Permits a state to provide tax incentives for production of electricity from (1) coal mined in the state and used in a facility, if such production meets federal and state laws and if the facility uses clean coal technology, including scrubbers; (2) a renewable source such as wind, solar, or biomass; or (3) ethanol. Declares that any such state tax incentive shall (1) be considered to be a reasonable regulation of commerce, and (2) not be considered to impose an undue burden on interstate commerce or to otherwise impair, restrain, or discriminate, against interstate commerce. Introduced January 26, 2005; referred to Committee on Energy and Commerce and Committee on Judiciary.

H.R. 388 (Kaptur)

Biofuels Energy Independence Act of 2005. Authorizes the Secretary of Agriculture to make and guarantee loans for biofuel production, distribution, development, and storage. Sets forth loan eligibility provisions. Directs the Secretary to establish a related revolving fund. Authorizes the Secretary to administer a Biofuels Feedstocks Energy Reserve to (1) provide feedstocks in furtherance of biofuel-based energy production; and (2) support the biofuels energy industry when production is at risk due to feedstock reductions or commodity price increases. Sets forth related provisions respecting commercial commodity purchases, release of commodity stocks, and storage payments. Introduced January 26, 2005; referred to Committee on Agriculture. Senate bill introduced March 15; referred to Committee on Energy and Natural Resources.

H.R. 423 (Terry)

Homeland Infrastructure Power Security and Assurance Incentives Act of 2005. Authorizes the Secretary of Energy to establish an Advanced Power System Technology Incentive Program of incentive payments to eligible owners or operators to (1) support deployment of new advanced power system technologies such as fuel cells, turbines, hybrid, and storage system power technologies; and (2) improve and protect certain critical governmental, industrial, and commercial processes. Requires such funding to be used to increase power generation through enhanced operational, economic, and environmental performance. Introduced January 26, 2005; referred to Committee on Energy and Commerce.

H.R. 424 (Terry)

Energy Efficiency Investment Act of 2005. Amends the Internal Revenue Code to allow a tax credit for up to 25% of the cost of certain energy efficient property installed in business and residential properties. Introduced January 26, 2005; referred to Committee on Ways and Means.

H.R. 444 (Issa)

Hybrid Vehicle HOV Access Act. Amends Federal highway law to authorize a State to permit a hybrid vehicle with fewer than two occupants to operate in high occupancy vehicle (HOV) lanes. Defines "hybrid vehicle" as a motor vehicle (1) that draws propulsion energy from onboard sources of stored energy which are both an internal combustion or heat engine using combustible fuel and a rechargeable energy storage system; and (2) which (in the case of a passenger automobile or light truck) for 2002 and later models meets certain clean air requirements. Introduced February 1, 2005; referred to Committee on Transportation and Infrastructure.

H.R. 610 (Biggert)

Energy Research, Development, Demonstration, and Commercial Application Act of 2005. Directs the Secretary of Energy to establish R&D programs in (1) vehicles, buildings, and industrial processes; (2) renewable energy research; (3) civilian nuclear energy research; (4) fuel recycling technology; (5) fossil energy production, upgrading, conversion and consumption; (6) oil and gas research; (7) fuel cells; and (8) ultra-deepwater and unconventional natural gas. Instructs the Secretary to (1) plan programs directly related to fuel cells or hydrogen; and (2) conduct programs to address hydrogen production from diverse energy sources. Directs the President to establish an interagency task force to work toward fuel infrastructure for hydrogen and hydrogen-carrier fuels, including buses and other fleet transportation. Establishes the Hydrogen Technical and Fuel Cell Advisory Committee. Directs the Secretary to establish a competitive grant pilot program for acquisition of (1) alternative fueled vehicles or fuel cell vehicles; (2) hybrid vehicles; and (3) ultra-low sulfur diesel vehicles. Directs the Administrator of the Environmental Protection Agency to establish a grant program for (1) the replacement of certain school buses with alternative fuel school buses and ultra-low sulfur diesel fuel school buses; and (2) installation of retrofit technologies for diesel school buses. Instructs the Secretary to enter into cooperative agreements (1) with private sector fuel cell bus developers for the development of fuel cell-powered school buses; and (2) government entities using natural gas-powered school buses and private sector fuel cell bus developers to demonstrate the use of fuel cell-powered school buses. Directs the Secretary to (1) establish a fuel cell transit bus demonstration program; and (2) award grants to universities for the establishment of Centers of Excellence for Energy Systems of the Future to advance new clean coal technologies. Introduced February 8, 2005; referred to House Committees on Science, Resources, and Energy and Commerce. Science Committee ordered to be reported February 10, 2005.

H.R. 612 (Biggert)

Energy Basic and Applied Sciences Act of 2005. Requires the Secretary of Energy to establish advisory committees to advise the separtment's applied programs in energy efficiency, renewable energy, and other areas. Directs the Secretary to establish a R&D program in: vehicles, buildings, and industrial processes; renewable energy research; fuel cells; and other areas. Introduced February 8, 2005; referred to Committees on Science, Resources, and Energy and Commerce.

H.R. 622 (Bono)/S. 326 (Smith)

Renewable Energy Production Incentive (REPI) Reform Act. Amends the Energy Policy Act of 1992 to modify renewable energy production incentive payment guidelines to provide that if there are insufficient appropriations to make full payments for electric production from all qualified renewable energy facilities in any given year, the Secretary of Energy shall assign 60% of appropriated funds for that year to facilities that use solar, wind, geothermal, or closed-loop (dedicated energy crops) biomass technologies to generate electricity, and assign the remaining 40% to other projects. Redefines a qualified renewable energy facility as one (1) owned by certain tax-exempt electricity-generating cooperatives, certain public utilities, a state, territorial, or local governments or an Indian tribal government; and (2) which may involve electricity generation by landfill gas. Extends through FY2015 the deadline for first use of a facility eligible for incentive payments. House bill introduced February 8, 2005; referred to Committee on Energy and Commerce. Senate bill introduced February 9, 2005; referred to Committee on Energy and Natural Resources.

H.R. 626 (Camp)

VEHICLE Technology Act of 2005. Amends the Internal Revenue Code to repeal the phaseouts of the tax credit for qualified electric vehicles and of the tax deduction for clean-fuel vehicles. Allows a tax credit for investment in certain alternative motor vehicles, including fuel cell vehicles, advanced lean burn technology motor vehicles, hybrid motor vehicles, alternative fuel motor vehicles, and mixed-fuel vehicles. Sets forth formulas for determining the amount of the credit based on various factors, including vehicle weight and fuel efficiency ratings. Modifies the tax deduction for clean-fuel vehicles and certain refueling property to (1) extend the terminating date for such deduction through 2009, and through 2012 for hydrogen-related property; (2) increase to $150,000 the cost limitation for the deduction; and (3) extend the deduction to nonbusiness property. Introduced February 8, 2005; referred to Committee on Ways and Means.

H.R. 705 (Gilchrest)/S. 889 (Feinstein)

Automobile Fuel Economy Act of 2005. Sets forth certain increased average fuel economy standards for certain light trucks, automobiles (up to 10,000 pounds gross vehicle weight), and certain classes of vehicles in the federal fleet that are manufactured or purchased after specified dates. House bill introduced February 9, 2005; referred to Committee on Energy and Commerce and Committee on Government Reform. Senate bill introduced April 21, 2005; referred to Committee on Commerce, Science, and Transportation.

H.R. 722 (Oberstar)

Securing Transportation Energy Efficiency for Tomorrow Act of 2005. Amends the Federal Property and Administrative Services Act of 1949 to authorize the Administrator of General Services to establish a program for the procurement and installation of photovoltaic solar electric systems for electric production in public buildings. Directs the Architect of the Capitol to evaluate the energy infrastructure of the Capitol Complex to determine how it could be augmented to become more energy efficient, using photovoltaic solar energy systems, district-heating, and other unconventional and renewable energy resources. Amends federal transportation law to (1) direct the Secretary of Transportation (Secretary) to establish a program of grants to state and local governments for fuel conservation projects; (2) authorize the Secretary to make grants for fuel cell bus technology projects; and (3) require environmental impact statements for federal-aid highway and transit projects to consider energy impacts as an environmental project consequence. Directs the Secretary to establish (1) a Conserve By Bicycling pilot program for projects to encourage the use of bicycles in place of motor vehicles; and (2) a specified public-private research partnership dedicated to advancement of railroad technology, efficiency, and safety owned by the Federal Railroad Administration and operated in the private sector. Directs (1) the Secretary to establish a pilot clean airport bus replacement and fleet expansion grant program; and (2) the Administrator of the Federal Aviation Administration to establish a public-private research partnership to develop a clean ground demonstrator engine utilizing specified National Aeronautics and Space Administration-developed technologies. Directs the Secretary to establish a public-private research partnership to develop and demonstrate technologies that increase fuel economy, reduce emissions, and lower costs of marine transportation, as well as the efficiency of intermodal transfers. Directs the Secretary of the Army to study and report to Congress on the potential for reduced fossil fuel consumption through an increase in U.S. hydropower capabilities. Amends the Internal Revenue Code to exclude from gross income as a qualifying transportation fringe benefit a commuting allowance of $75 per month for individuals who bicycle, carpool, or car-share to work. Introduced February 9, 2005; referred to Committee on Energy and Commerce and Committee on Government Reform.

H.R. 737 (Woolsey)

Renewable Energy and Energy Efficiency Act of 2005. Declares it shall be policy of the United States that its research, development, demonstration, and commercial applications programs be designed to enable 20% of domestic energy generated from stationary sources to be generated from nonhydropower renewable energy sources by the year 2020. Prescribes research and development program goals to implement such policy in connection with enhanced (1) renewable energy; (2) energy efficiency; and (3) aeronautical system energy. Directs the Secretary of Energy to (1) submit to Congress an assessment of renewable energy resources available for commercial application; and (2) implement a Next Generation Lighting Initiative for advanced solid-state lighting technologies based on white light-emitting diodes. Requires the Director of the Office of Science and Technology Policy to establish (1) an interagency group to develop a National Building Performance Initiative; and (2) an advisory committee to analyze and provide recommendations on potential private sector roles and participation in the Initiative. Directs the Secretary of Energy to (1) commission an independent assessment of innovative financing techniques to facilitate construction of new renewable energy and energy efficiency facilities; (2) establish a demonstration program for innovative technologies for renewable energy sources in buildings owned or operated by a state or local government; (3) provide assistance to small businesses and startup companies for the commercial application of renewable energy and energy efficiency technologies developed by or with support from the Department of Energy; (4) establish an education and outreach program on renewable energy and energy efficiency technologies; and (5) establish a competitive matching grant pilot program for voluntary local government programs that seek to promote innovative energy efficiency technologies and processes to reduce the industrial use of water and the discharge of wastewater from commercial and industrial entities. Introduced February 9, 2005; referred to Committee on Energy and Commerce.

H.R. 759 (Gilchrest)

Climate Stewardship Act of 2005. Establishes various policies for curbing greenhouse gas emissions that include several energy-efficiency and renewable energy measures. Introduced February 10, 2005; referred to Committee on Science and to Committee on Energy and Commerce.

H.R. 779 (Radanovich)

Federal Hydropower Enhancement Act of 2005. Directs the Secretary of the Interior, the Secretary of Energy, and the Secretary of the Army to study and report to Congress on the potential for increasing electric power production capability at federally owned or operated facilities for water regulation, storage, and conveyance. Introduced February 10, 2005; referred to Committee on Resources and to Committee on Transportation and Infrastructure.

H.R. 971 (Simmons)

Directs the Federal Energy Regulatory Commission to extend through May 30, 2007, the time period during which the licensee is required to commence construction for projects numbered 11547, 10822, and 10823 in the state of Connecticut. Requires the commission thereafter, upon licensee request, to extend the time period for construction of such project for two consecutive two-year periods. Directs the commission to reinstate the licenses for such projects effective as of their respective expiration dates. States that the first authorized extension for each such project shall take effect on its expiration date. Introduced February 17, 2005; referred to Committee on Energy and Commerce.

H.R. 983 (T. Udall)

Amends the Public Utility Regulatory Policies Act of 1978 to prescribe guidelines for a Federal Renewable Portfolio Standard (RPS) for calendar years 2008 through 2037. Specifies a schedule of graduated annual percentages of a supplier's base amount, from 1% in 2008 up to 20% in 2027 and thereafter, that shall be generated from renewable energy resources. Authorizes a supplier to satisfy such requirements through the submission of renewable energy credits to the Secretary of Energy. Provides for energy credit trading or borrowing among suppliers. Directs the Secretary to (1) encourage federally owned utilities, municipally owned utilities, and rural electric cooperatives that sell electric energy to electric consumers for purposes other than resale to participate in the renewable portfolio standard program; and (2) establish by December 31, 2007, a state renewable energy account program. Introduced February 17, 2005; referred to Committee on Energy and Commerce.

H.R. 1103 (N. Johnson)

Fuel Efficiency Truth in Advertising Act of 2005. Directs the Administrator of the Environmental Protection Agency (EPA) to revise certain federal vehicle fuel economy test procedures to take into consideration higher speed limits, faster acceleration rates, variations in temperature, use of air conditioning, shorter city test cycle lengths, and the use of other fuel depleting features. Introduced March 3, 2005; referred to Committee on Energy and Commerce. Incorporated into H.R. 6 as floor amendment H.Amdt. 74 (as amended by H.Amdt. 75).

H.R. 1127 (T. Lee)

Renewable Energy Production Incentive (REPI) Reform and Reauthorization Act.. Makes equal incentives available from the Department of Energy (solar, wind, geothermal), Department of Agriculture (biomass), and Environmental Protection Agency (landfill gas). Introduced March 3, 2005; referred to Committee on Energy and Commerce.

H.R. 1158 (Hart)

Reauthorizes the Steel and Aluminum Energy Conservation and Technology Competitiveness Act of 1988. Modifies the list of priorities that the Secretary of Energy must consider in reviewing research and development activities for possible inclusion in the Steel Initiative Research Plan to include the development of (1) advanced sheet and bar steel; and (2) technologies that reduce greenhouse gas emissions. Introduced March 8, 2005; referred to Committee on Science.

H.R. 1212 (Weller)

Save America's Valuable Energy Resources Act of 2005. Amends the Internal Revenue Code to establish tax credits for (1) qualified energy efficient improvements to existing homes; and (2) the construction of qualified new energy efficient homes. Allows a tax deduction for energy efficient commercial building property expenditures. Introduced March 10; referred to Committees on Energy and Commerce, Ways and Means, and Science.

H.R. 1215 (Gingrey)

Green Chemistry Research and Development Act of 2005. Provision for grants to manufacturers includes measures that would increase energy efficiency. Introduced March 10, 2005; referred to Committee on Science.

H.R. 1255 (C. Peterson)

Clean Power Plant Act of 2005. Amends the Internal Revenue Code to extend until December 31, 2010, the tax credit for biodiesel used as fuel. Introduced March 10, 2005; referred to Committee on Ways and Means.

H.R. 1397 (N. Johnson)/S. 671 (Lieberman)

Establishes an investment tax credit for fuel cell equipment purchased for business and residential uses. The fuel cell must have a minimum capacity of 0.5 kilowatt (kw). The upper limit of the credit is $500 for each 0.5 kw, with a maximum of 30% of the total fuel cell cost. House bill introduced March 17, 2005; referred to Committee on Ways and Means. Senate bill introduced March 17, 2005; referred to Committee on Finance.

H.R. 1398 (Kaptur)

Amends the Clean Air Act to require that, after the year 2010, all gasoline sold in the United States for motor vehicles contain at least 10% ethanol and that all diesel fuel sold in the United States for motor vehicles contain at least 5% Biodiesel. Introduced March 17, 2005; referred to Committee on Energy and Commerce.

H.R. 1421 (Nussle)

Resource Efficient Appliance Incentives Act of 2005. Creates an equipment production credit for 2005 through 2010 that ranges from $50 to

$150 per unit for clothes washers and refrigerators that meet certain energy-efficiency criteria. The total value of credits is limited by a dollar amount and by a percent of gross revenue. Introduced March 17, 2005; referred to Committee on Ways and Means.

H.R. 1451 (Waxman)

Clean Smokestacks Act of 2005. Amends the Clean Air Act (CAA) to require the Administrator of the Environmental Protection Agency (EPA) to promulgate regulations to achieve specified reductions in aggregate emissions of sulfur dioxide, nitrogen oxide, carbon dioxide, and mercury from powerplants (electric generation facilities with a nameplate capacity of 15 megawatts or more that use a combustion device to generate electricity for sale) by January 1, 2010. States that regulations promulgated under this act may require additional emissions reductions if the Administrator determines that the specified reductions are not reasonably anticipated to protect public health or welfare. Directs the Administrator to coordinate with other federal and state agencies to increase energy efficiency, to increase the use of renewable energy, and to implement cost saving advanced demand and supply side policies. Requires powerplants, on the later of the date 30 years after the powerplant commenced operation or five years after this act's enactment, to comply with the most recent new source performance standards under CAA provisions regarding air quality and emissions limitations and with specified requirements for modified sources. Introduced March 17, 2005; referred to Committee on Energy and Commerce.

H.R. 1482 (Wynn)

Hydrogen Liberty Act. Authorizes $3.9 billion over 10 years for research and development of advanced nuclear reactor ($1.3 billion), solar energy ($1.3 billion), and wind energy ($1.3 billion) technologies for the production of hydrogen. The bill would create 15 demonstration projects, five for each of the three technologies. Introduced April 5, 2005; referred to Committee on Science and Committee on Energy and Commerce.

H.R. 1511 (Foley)

Extends the renewable energy electricity production tax credit (PTC) for wind energy for five years. Introduced April 6, 2005; referred to Committee on Ways and Means.

H.R. 1530 (Shadegg)

Section 3(e) creates a 1.5cent/kwh incentive (maximum $1 million) for increased hydropower capacity at existing non-federal dams. Also, for qualified efficiency improvements (minimum 3% improvement) at existing dams, Section 4 creates incentive worth up to 10% of the capital cost. Introduced April 6, 2005; referred to Committee on Energy and Commerce.

H.R. 1533 (T. Davis)

Federal Energy Management Improvement Act of 2005. Title I has provisions for energy reduction goals, energy-efficient equipment procurement, and ESPCs. Title II requires purchases of renewable energy. Title VII has provisions for alternative fuel use. Introduced April 8, 2005; referred to Committee on Government Reform and Committee on Energy and Commerce. Committee on Government Reform held markup and ordered reported April 13.

H.R. 1541 (Thomas)

Enhanced Energy Infrastructure and Technology Tax Act of 2005. Referred to Committee on Ways and Means April 12, 2005. Committee held markup April 13. Reported (H.Rept. 109-45) April 18. Incorporated into H.R. 6.

H.R. 1608 (Herseth)/S. 650 (Lugar)

Fuels Security Act of 2005. Section 101 increases the renewable fuel standard (RFS) to 8 billion gallons by 2012. Section 102 directs federal agencies purchases of gasoline to include 10% ethanol-blended gasoline within five years. It also directs agencies' purchases of diesel fuel to include 2% biodiesel in five years and 20% biodiesel in 10 years. House bill introduced April 13, 2005; referred to Committee on Energy and Commerce. Senate bill, introduced March 17, 2005; referred to the Committee on Environment and Public Works.

H.R. 1612 (Kaptur)

Establishes ethanol (10% blend) and biodiesel (2% rising to 20% over 10 years) fuel requirements for the federal fleet. Introduced April 13, 2005; referred to Committee on Government Reform.

H.R. 1640 (Barton)

Energy Policy Act of 2005. Contains titles on energy efficiency, renewable energy, alternative fuels, and many other non-tax energy policy areas. On April 14, 2005, referred to Committees on Energy and Commerce, Resources, Science, and several other committees. Incorporated into H.R. 6.

H.R. 1705 (Shadegg)

Establishes a program to support deployment of idle reduction and energy conservation technologies for heavy-duty vehicles, and for other purposes. Introduced April 19, 2005; referred to Committee on Energy and Commerce and Committee on Transportation and Infrastructure.

H.R. 1706 (Shadegg)

Directs the Secretary of Energy to conduct a program in partnership with the private sector to accelerate efforts of domestic automobile manufacturers to manufacture commercially available competitive hybrid vehicle technologies in the United States. Introduced April 19, 2005; referred to Committee on Science and Committee on Energy and Commerce.

H.R. 1744 (Ruppersberger)

Common Sense Automobile Efficiency Act of 2005. Repeals phaseouts of tax credits for qualified electric and clean-fueled vehicles. Introduced April 20, 2005; referred to Committee on Ways and Means.

H.R. 1750 (Boehlert)

Grand Canyon Hydrogen-Powered Transportation Demonstration Act of 2005. Directs DOE (in cooperation with Department of Interior) to research, develop, and demonstrate, in cooperation with affected and related industries, a hydrogen-based alternative public transportation system suitable for operations within Grand Canyon National Park and other sensitive resource areas. Introduced April 21, 2005; referred to Committee on Science.

H.R. 1797 (McMorris)/S. 881 (Cantwell)

Spokane Tribe of Indians of the Spokane Reservation Grand Coulee Dam Equitable Compensation Settlement Act. Establishes in the Treasury the Spokane Tribe of Indians Settlement Fund. Requires the payment of compensation to the Spokane Business Council for the use of tribal lands for the generation of hydropower from the Grand Coulee Dam. Requires the use of such funds, in part, for a Cultural Resource Repository and Interpretive Center concerning the culture and history of the Spokane Tribe. Directs the Administrator of the Bonneville Power Administration to make specified settlement payments to the Spokane Tribe. Allows payments made to the Spokane Business Council or Spokane Tribe to be used or invested by the

Business Council in the same manner and for the same purposes as other Spokane Tribal governmental funds. Directs the Secretary of the Interior to transfer administrative jurisdiction from the Bureau of Reclamation to the Bureau of Indian Affairs over certain land located within the exterior boundaries of the Spokane Indian Reservation and certain other land located on the south bank of the Spokane River. Provides that payments by the Secretary and the Administrator and restoration of ownership of land in trust constitute full satisfaction of the claim of the Spokane Tribe to a fair share of the annual hydropower revenues generated by the Grand Coulee Dam project for the past and continued use of land of the Spokane Tribe for the production of hydropower at Grand Coulee Dam. House bill introduced April 21, 2005; referred to Committee on Resources. Ordered reported May 18. Senate bill introduced April 21, 2005; referred to Committee on Indian Affairs.

H.R. 1815 (Hunter)/S. 1042 (Warner)

National Defense Authorization Act for FY2006. Section 2402 authorizes funding for energy conservation projects. House bill introduced April 26, 2005; referred to Committee on Armed Services. Includes $50 million authorization. Reported (H.Rept. 109-89) May 20. Passed House May 25. Senate bill introduced May 12, 2005; referred to Committee on Armed Services. Includes $60 million authorization. Reported (S.Rept. 109-69) May 17.

H.R. 1834 (Cunningham)/S. 680 (Snowe)

Efficient Energy Through Certified Technologies and Electricity Reliability (EFFECTER) Act of 2005. Section 101 creates an income tax deduction ($2.25 per square foot maximum) for energy efficiency measures that reduce commercial building energy use by 50% below the American Society of Heating, Refrigeration, and Air Conditioning Equipment Association's (ASHRAE's) 90.1 industry energy efficiency standard. Section 102 establishes an investment tax credit for energy efficiency measures in new home construction that reduce energy use by 30% ($1,000 maximum) or by 50% ($2,000 maximum). Section 103 sets a tax deduction for business use of solar hot water, photovoltaics, heat pumps (gas, electric, ground source), furnaces, and boilers. It also creates a tax deduction ($6,000 maximum) for such equipment used in residential rental properties that reduces energy use by 50% (pro-rated for smaller energy reductions). Section 104 creates a nonbusiness tax credit ($2,000 maximum) for equipment that reduces energy use by 50%. Section 105 establishes an investment tax credit available over four years to combined heat and power (CHP or cogeneration) systems smaller than 15 megawatts (MW) that satisfy certain efficiency standards. Section 201 sets energy efficiency test procedures and standards for a variety of equipment and products. For battery chargers and external power supplies, the Secretary of Energy has three years to determine whether standards are needed. Further, standards (or requirements) are set for vending machines, commercial refrigerators and freezers, illuminated exit signs, torchieres, distribution transformers, traffic signal modules, unit heaters, compact fluorescent light bulbs, ceiling fans, dehumidifiers, spray valves, and furnace fans. Section 202 directs the Secretary of Energy to issue a rulemaking that assesses effectiveness of labeling requirements and a rulemaking to set labeling requirements for additional consumer products (including distribution transformers). Section 203 sets test procedures and standards for commercial package air conditioners and heating equipment. Section 204 creates standards for commercial refrigerators and freezers. Section 301 directs federal agencies to procure EPA Energy Star and DOE Federal Energy Management Program- (FEMP-) designated energy equipment, where it is cost-effective. Section 302 permanently extends the authority for federal agencies to enter energy saving performance contracts (ESPCs). Section 303 sets federal building energy performance standards by updating the baseline from the 1992 Council of American Building Officials (CABO) to the 2003 International Energy Conservation Code (IECC). Further, it directs the Secretary of Energy to require new federal buildings to achieve a 30% energy reduction, provided it is cost-effective on a life-cycle basis. Section 401 modifies the Public Housing Capital Fund to include certain energy and water use efficiency improvements. Section 402 directs the Secretary of Housing and Urban Development (HUD) to provide grants for certain energy and water efficiency improvements to multifamily housing projects. Section 403 directs public housing agencies to purchase cost-effective Energy Star or FEMP-designated appliances and products. Section 404 changes the energy efficiency standards and codes for public housing from CABO to the 2003 International Energy Conservation Code, where HUD finds it cost-effective. House bill introduced April 26, 2005; referred to Committees on Energy and Commerce, Ways and Means, and Financial Services. Senate bill introduced March 17, 2005; referred to Committee on Finance.

H.R. 2070 (Kucinich)

Creates an income tax credit for purchases of fuel-efficient passenger vehicles and establishes grants for mass transit. Introduced May 4, 2005;

referred to Committee on Ways and Means and Committee on Transportation and Infrastructure.

H.R. 2358 (M. Udall)

Aeronautics Research and Development Revitalization Act of 2005. Section 201 directs the National Aeronautics and Space Administration (NASA) to set 10-year technology improvement goals, which include a 25% reduction in fuel use for medium- and long-range commercial aircraft. Introduced May 12, 2005; referred to Committee on Science.

H.R. 2419 (Hobson)

Energy and Water Development Appropriations Act, 2006. Includes funding for DOE's energy efficiency and renewable energy programs. Committee on Appropriations reported (H.Rept. 109-86) May 18, 2005. Passed House, amended, May 24.

H.R. 2498 (Hulshof)/S. 1076 (Lincoln)

Extends through December 31, 2010, the tax credit for biodiesel used as fuel and the excise credits for biodiesel mixtures and biodiesel used to produce biodiesel mixtures. House bill introduced May 19, 2005; referred to Committee on Ways and Means. Senate bill introduced May 19, 2005; referred to Committee on Finance.

H.R. 2665 (Engel)

Encourages the availability and use of motor vehicles that have improved fuel efficiency, in order to reduce oil imports. Introduced May 26, 2005; referred to Committee on Ways and Means, Committee on Financial Services, and Committee on Energy and Commerce.

H.R. 2751 (Andrews)

FHA Energy Efficiency Act. Amends Section 526 of the National Housing Act to provide that any certification of a property for meeting energy efficiency requirements for mortgage insurance must be conducted by an individual certified by an accredited home energy rating system provider. Introduced June 7, 2005; referred to Committee on Financial Services.

H.R. 2794 (R. Lewis)

Clean Energy Bonds Act of 2005. Establishes a nonrefundable tax credit to holders of qualified bonds issued to finance certain clean energy projects. Qualified borrowers include electric coops, governmental bodies, and the

Tennessee Valley Authority. Unused credits can be carried over for one year. Introduced June 8, 2005; referred to Committee on Ways and Means.

H.R. 2828 (Inslee)

New Apollo Energy Act of 2005. Includes incentives for fuel-efficient vehicles, including tax credits for the purchase of hybrid, alternative-fuel, low-emission advanced diesel, and fuel-cell vehicles. Also, it provides $11.5 billion in tax credits for the automotive and aerospace industries to develop new fuel efficient automobiles and planes, retool existing plants, and construct new plants to manufacture energy-efficient vehicles. Establishes an alternative fuel vehicle purchase requirement for government agencies; tax credits for the installation of alternative refueling properties and for the retail sale of alternative fuels; a renewable fuels standard is set at 8 billion gallons by 2013; modifies the tax credit for qualified electric vehicles; and creates loans for schools to buy high-efficiency vehicles. New Apollo provides $49 billion in government loan guarantees for the construction of clean-energy generation facilities that will produce power from wind, solar, geothermal, biomass, oceans, coal with carbon-sequestration technology, and other sources. Commits $10.5 billion to research-and-development and investment tax credits for clean energy-producing operations. In addition, it includes a 10-year extension of the current renewable energy production tax credit (PTC). Calls for reductions in daily domestic oil consumption of 600,000 barrels a day by 2010; 1,700,000 barrels by 2015; and 3,000,000 barrels by 2020. Caps U.S. emissions of greenhouse gases while allowing companies to purchase and trade credits among themselves to ensure the most cost-effective reductions, and funds research to help industries shift to cleaner operations. Further, provides $7 billion in loan guarantees for the development of clean coal power plants. Funds new federal research into advanced clean technologies, and creates a government-funded risk pool to help start-up clean-energy companies commercialize their products. Establishes a Renewable Portfolio Standard (RPS) requiring all utilities, by 2021, to produce 10% of their electricity from renewable energy sources. Creates national net-metering and interconnection standards for homeowners. Also, it includes provisions to make it revenue-neutral, by reducing corporate tax shelters and loopholes, and by auctioning some of the allowances under the carbon dioxide trading program. Introduced June 9, 2005; referred to Committee on Ways and Means, Committee on Energy and Commerce, and several other committees.

Senate Bills (with House Companions)

S. 10 (Domenici)

Energy Policy Act of 2005. Section 102 sets a goal for 20% energy reduction in federal facilities by 2015. Section 104 requires federal agency purchases of EPA Energy Star and FEMP-designated products. Section 105 extends ESPCs through 2016. Section 123 authorizes funding to states for rebates to support the cost premium for residential purchases of Energy Star products. Sections 135 and 136 establish energy efficiency standards for a variety of consumer products and commercial equipment. Title I also sets out several energy efficiency provisions for public housing. Title VII has provisions for hybrid, fuel cell, and electric vehicles; and revises and extends some aspects of fuel economy standards. Title IX reauthorizes DOE energy efficiency R&D programs. Section 1253 would, under certain conditions, terminate PURPA cogeneration requirements. For renewables, reauthorizes REPI and sets renewable fuels purchasing requirement for federal agencies. Committee on Energy and Natural Resources reported (S.Rept. 109-121) June 9, 2005.

S. 35 (Conrad)

Extends the renewable energy production tax credit (PTC) for facilities until January 1, 2011. Introduced January 24, 2005; referred to Committee on Finance.

S. 129 (Talent)/H.R. 325 (Graves)

Hybrid HOV Access Act. Allows energy-efficient and low-emission vehicles to use HOV facilities. Senate bill introduced January 24, 2005; referred to Committee on Environment and Public Works. House bill introduced January 25, 2005; referred to Committee on Transportation and Infrastructure.

S. 131 (Inhofe)

Clear Skies Act of 2005. Amends the Clean Air Act to reduce air pollution through expansion of cap and trade programs. Section 413 preserves an energy conservation and renewable energy reserve of 300,000 sulfur dioxide emission reduction allowances, which could be used to help meet air pollution reduction requirements. Introduced January 24, 2005; referred to Committee on Environment and Public Works. Committee held markup March 9, 2005, but the bill failed to pass Committee on a tie (9-9) vote.

S. 150 (Jeffords)

Clean Power Act of 2005. Requires the Environmental Protection Agency (EPA) to (1) set regulations to reduce emissions of sulfur dioxide, nitrogen oxides, carbon dioxide, and mercury from certain electric generation facilities by January 1, 2010; and (2) establish an emission allowance tracking and transfer system for these emissions. Section 707 directs that up to 20% of allowances for reductions of sulfur dioxide, nitrogen oxides, and carbon dioxide can be obtained from energy efficiency and renewable energy sources. Introduced January 25, 2005; referred to Committee on Environment and Public Works.

S. 244 (Thomas)

Authorizes the Federal Energy Regulatory Commission (FERC) to extend, at the request of the project licensee, the deadline for commencement of construction of hydroelectric project number 1651 in the State of Wyoming for three consecutive two-year periods from the expiration of the extension originally issued by the Commission. Introduced February 1, 2005; referred to Committee on Energy and Natural Resources. Reported (S.Rept. 109-32) March 10.

S. 269 (Kerry)

Small Business and Farm Energy Emergency Relief Act of 2005. Section 3 makes loans available to small business to convert from heating fuel to alternative energy sources that may include biowaste, geothermal energy, solar energy, wind energy, and fuel cells. Introduced February 2, 2005; referred to Committee on Small Business and Entrepreneurship.

S. 326 (Smith)/H.R. 622 (Bono)

Renewable Energy Production Incentive (REPI) Reform Act. Amends the Energy Policy Act of 1992 to modify renewable energy production incentive payment guidelines to provide that if there are insufficient appropriations to make full payments for electric production from all qualified renewable energy facilities in any given year, the Secretary of Energy shall assign 60% of appropriated funds for that year to facilities that use solar, wind, geothermal, or closed-loop (dedicated energy crops) biomass technologies to generate electricity, and assign the remaining 40% to other projects. Redefines a qualified renewable energy facility as one (1) owned by certain tax-exempt electricity-generating cooperatives, certain public utilities, a State, territorial, or local governments or an Indian tribal government; and (2) which may involve electricity generation by landfill gas. Extends through FY2015 the deadline for first use of a facility eligible for incentive payments. Senate bill introduced February 9, 2005; referred to Committee on Energy and Natural Resources. House bill introduced February 8, 2005; referred to Committee on Energy and Commerce.

S. 373 (Harkin)

Renewable Hydrogen Passenger Vehicle Act of 2005. Amends the Farm Security and Rural Investment Act of 2002 to direct the Secretary of Energy, in coordination with the Secretary of Agriculture, to conduct a three-year program to develop and demonstrate the cost-effective operation of a fleet of at least 10 direct hydrogen passenger vehicles based on existing commercial technology under which the hydrogen is derived from ethanol or other domestic low-cost transportable renewable feedstocks. Introduced February 14, 2005; referred to Committee on Energy and Natural Resources.

S. 386 (Hagel)

Climate Change Technology Deployment in Developing Countries Act of 2005. Section 2 includes cogeneration and renewable energy as eligible technologies for demonstration projects that could help developing countries reduce greenhouse gas emissions. Introduced February 15, 2005; referred to Committee on Foreign Relations.

S. 387 (Hagel)

Climate Change Technology Tax Incentives Act of 2005. Section 201 expresses the sense of the Senate that (1) the renewable energy production tax credit (PTC) should be extended through 2010; and (2) the research investment tax credit should be increased and made permanent. Senate bill introduced February 15, 2005; referred to Committee on Finance.

S. 388 (Hagel)

Climate Change Technology Deployment and Infrastructure Credit Act of 2005. Credit-based financial incentives would be available to support demonstration projects for cogeneration, renewable energy, and other "climate technologies." Introduced March 15, 2005; referred to Committee on Energy and Natural Resources.

S. 426 (Jeffords)

Electric Reliability Security Act of 2005. Contains several provisions to support energy efficiency and renewable energy, including a system benefit fund (Section 201) to fund state energy efficiency and renewable energy programs, an energy efficiency performance standard (Section 202) to reduce electricity demand by 10% over 10 years, appliance efficiency standards (Section 203) for central air conditioners and heat pumps, and loan guarantees (Section 204) for fuel cells, combined heat and power (CHP), energy efficiency, and several types of renewables. Also, Title III has a provision for net metering. Introduced February 17, 2005; referred to Committee on Energy and Natural Resources.

S. 427 (Jeffords)

Renewable Energy Investment Act of 2005. Creates a federal renewable portfolio standard by amending the Public Utility Regulatory Policies Act of 1978 to require retail electric suppliers to submit to the Secretary of Energy renewable energy credits in an amount equal to the required annual percentage of the retail electric supplier's total amount of kilowatt-hours of non-hydropower electricity sold to retail consumers during the previous calendar year (excluding incremental hydropower). States that a renewable energy credit that is not used to satisfy the minimum requirement for that year may be carried over for use within the next two years. Specifies a schedule of the minimum percentage of renewable energy sources that must be used to generate the total amount of non-hydropower electricity sold by each retail electric supplier during a calendar year (excluding incremental hydropower). Directs the Secretary to (1) establish a program to issue, monitor the sale or exchange of, and track renewable energy credits; and (2) make funds available under this act to State energy agencies for grant programs for renewable energy research and development, and for loan guarantees to encourage construction of renewable energy facilities. Introduced February 17, 2005; referred to Committee on Energy and Natural Resources.

S. 436 (Akaka)

Directs the Secretary of Energy to assess the economic implications of the dependence of the State of Hawaii on oil as its principal source of energy, including the technical and economic feasibility of increasing the contribution of renewable energy resources for generation of electricity, on an island-by-island basis; and the technical and economic feasibility of using renewable energy sources (including hydrogen) for ground, marine, and air transportation energy applications to displace the use of refined petroleum products. Introduced February 17, 2005; referred to Committee on Energy and Natural Resources.

S. 502 (Coleman)

Rural Renaissance Act. Allows funds developed for a "Rural Renaissance Trust Account" to be used for renewable energy projects on farms. Introduced March 3, 2005; referred to Committee on Finance.

S. 542 (Dorgan)

Amends the Internal Revenue Code to (1) extend through 2010 the renewable energy electricity production tax credit (PTC) for certain renewable resources (e.g., wind, biomass, poultry waste); (2) allow certain organizations, including tax-exempt organizations, state and local governments, and Indian tribal governments, to sell unused amounts of such tax credit. Introduced March 7, 2005; referred to Committee on Finance.

S. 587 (Dayton)

Requires that automobiles and light trucks manufactured after model year 2006 be able to operate on a fuel mixture that is at least 85% ethanol. Introduced March 10; referred to Committee on Commerce, Science, and Transportation.

S. 606 (Thune)

Reliable Fuels Act. Sets a goal to increase ethanol (including ethanol derived from cellulosic biomass) use from 3.8 billion gallons in 2006 to 6.0 billion gallons in 2012. Introduced March 11, 2005; referred to Committee on Environment and Public Works. Ordered to be reported, March 16, 2005.

S. 610 (Talent)/H.R. 36 (S. King)

Amends the Internal Revenue Code to revise the tax credit for biodiesel used as fuel to include a credit for the production of agri-biodiesel fuel equal to 10 cents for each gallon produced. Limits (1) the amount of qualified agri-biodiesel production of a producer to 15 million gallons for any taxable year; and (2) eligible producers to those with an annual productive capacity not exceeding 60 million gallons. Revises the small ethanol producer tax credit to (1) expand the eligibility of small ethanol producers for the credit; (2) exclude the credit from the definition of passive activity credit; and (3) exclude credit amounts from inclusion in gross income. Senate bill introduced March 11, 2005; referred to Committee on Finance. House bill introduced January 4, 2005; referred to Committee on Ways and Means.

S. 650 (Lugar)/H.R. 1608 (Herseth)

Fuels Security Act of 2005. Section 101 increases the renewable fuel standard (RFS) to 8 billion gallons by 2012. Section 102 directs federal agencies purchases of gasoline to include 10% ethanol-blended gasoline within five years. It also directs agencies' purchases of diesel fuel to include 2% biodiesel in five years and 20% biodiesel in 10 years. Senate bill introduced March 17, 2005; referred to the Committee on Environment and Public Works. House bill introduced April 13, 2005; referred to the Committee on Energy and Commerce.

S. 665 (Dorgan)

Hydrogen and Fuel Cell Technology Act of 2005. Authorizes $2.3 billion over 10 years for hydrogen supply R&D programs and $1.7 billion over 10 years for fuel cell technology R&D programs. Further, over 10 years, it also authorizes $2.7 billion for vehicle demonstration programs, $900 million for market transition programs, $225 million for federal procurement programs, and $55 million for regulatory programs. Introduced March 17, 2005; referred to Committee on Energy and Natural Resources.

S. 671 (Lieberman)/H.R. 1397 (N. Johnson)

Establishes an investment tax credit for fuel cell equipment purchased for business and residential uses. The fuel cell must have a minimum capacity of 0.5 kilowatt (kw). The upper limit of the credit is $500 for each 0.5 kw, with a maximum of 30% of the total fuel cell cost. Senate bill introduced March 17, 2005; referred to Committee on Finance. House bill introduced March 17, 2005; referred to Committee on Ways and Means.

S. 680 (Snowe)/H.R. 1834

Efficient Energy Through Certified Technologies and Electricity Reliability (EFFECTER) Act of 2005. Section 101 creates an income tax deduction ($2.25 per square foot maximum) for energy efficiency measures that reduce commercial building energy use by 50% below the American Society of Heating, Refrigeration, and Air Conditioning Equipment Association's (ASHRAE's) 90.1 industry energy efficiency standard. Section 102 establishes an investment tax credit for energy efficiency measures in new home construction that reduce energy use by 30% ($1,000 maximum) or by 50% ($2,000 maximum). Section 103 sets a tax deduction for business use of solar hot water, photovoltaics, heat pumps (gas, electric, ground source), furnaces, and boilers. It also creates a tax deduction ($6,000 maximum) for such equipment used in residential rental properties that reduces energy use by 50% (pro-rated for smaller energy reductions). Section 104 creates a nonbusiness tax credit ($2,000 maximum) for equipment that reduces energy use by 50%. Section 105 establishes an investment tax credit available over four years to combined heat and power (CHP or cogeneration) systems smaller than 15 megawatts (MW) that satisfy certain efficiency standards. Section 201 sets energy efficiency test procedures and standards for a variety of equipment and products. For battery chargers and external power supplies, the Secretary of Energy has three years to determine whether standards are needed. Further, standards (or requirements) are set for vending machines, commercial refrigerators and freezers, illuminated exit signs, torchieres, distribution transformers, traffic signal modules, unit heaters, compact fluorescent light bulbs, ceiling fans, dehumidifiers, spray valves, and furnace fans. Section 202 directs the Secretary of Energy to issue a rulemaking that assesses effectiveness of labeling requirements and a rulemaking to set labeling requirements for additional consumer products (including distribution transformers). Section 203 sets test procedures and standards for commercial package air conditioners and heating equipment. Section 204 creates standards for commercial refrigerators and freezers. Section 301 directs federal agencies to procure energy equipment designated by EPA Energy Star and DOE Federal Energy Management Program (FEMP), where it is cost-effective. Section 302 permanently extends the authority for federal agencies to enter energy saving performance contracts (ESPCs). Section 303 sets federal building energy performance standards by updating the baseline from the 1992 Council of American Building Officials (CABO) to the 2003 International Energy Conservation Code (IECC). Further, it directs the Secretary of Energy to require new federal buildings to achieve a 30% energy reduction, provided it is cost-effective on a life-cycle basis. Section 401 modifies the Public Housing Capital Fund to include certain energy and water use efficiency improvements. Section 402 directs the Secretary of Housing and Urban Development (HUD) to provide grants for certain energy and water efficiency improvements to multifamily housing projects. Section 403 directs public housing agencies to purchase cost-effective Energy Star or FEMP-designated appliances and products. Section 404 changes the energy efficiency standards and codes for public housing from CABO to the 2003 International Energy Conservation Code, where HUD finds it cost-effective. Senate bill introduced March 17, 2005; referred to Committee on Finance. House bill introduced April 26, 2005; referred to Committees on Energy and Commerce, Ways and Means, and Financial Services.

S. 715 (Harkin)

Wind Power Tax Incentives Act of 2005. Amends the Internal Revenue Code to permit (1) individual taxpayers with adjusted gross incomes (taxable incomes in the case of corporate taxpayers) of $1 million or less to offset passive activity losses and credits from energy-producing wind facilities against regular income; and (2) tax-exempt cooperative organizations (including farmers' cooperatives) to apportion pro rata among their shareholders tax credits received for investment in energy-producing wind facilities. Introduced April 6, 2005; referred to Committee on Finance.

S. 726 (Alexander)

Natural Gas Price Reduction Act of 2005. Section 101 authorizes funding for an energy conservation public education initiative. Section 102 sets efficiency standards, test procedures, and labeling requirements for several types of residential and commercial equipment. Section 103 authorizes funding for distributed generation, solar energy, and biomass technologies. Section 104 authorizes funding to accelerate hydrogen and fuel cell development. Section 105 would, under certain conditions, repeal PURPA Section 210 requirements for cogeneration and small power facilities. Section 106 calls for a study of cogeneration and small power. Section 108 directs states to consider requiring net metering services for electric utility customers. Section 109 directs states to consider providing time-based schedules and meters for customers. Section 113 provides financial incentives to industry to encourage use of gasification equipment that uses biomass and other fuels. Introduced April 6, 2005; referred to Committee on Energy and Natural Resources.

S. 727 (Alexander)

Tax Incentives for the Natural Gas Price Reduction Act of 2005. Section 2 makes a 10% investment tax credit available over four years to combined heat and power (CHP or cogeneration) systems smaller than 50 megawatts (MW) that satisfy certain efficiency standards. Section 3 increases the investment tax credit for solar energy equipment from 10% to 30% for five years. Also, it extends the renewable energy production tax credit (PTC) for solar and geothermal energy for five years, and establishes a 30% tax credit ($7,500 maximum) for residential solar heating equipment. Section 4 has investment tax credits for residential solar (electric and water heating, 15%), wind (15%), and fuel cell (20%) equipment. It also creates a 20% investment tax credit ($2,000 maximum) to homeowners for retrofits to existing residential housing with energy efficient envelope components (insulation, windows, roofs, heating equipment); and an equipment tax credit (maximum $2,000) to home builders for envelope components that reduce home energy use by 30%. Section 4 also provides a tax credit to manufacturers ($60 million maximum) for energy-efficient clothes washers ($100 each) and refrigerators ($150 each). Further, Section 4 creates a tax deduction ($1.50 per square foot maximum) for energy efficient equipment in commercial buildings that reduces energy use by 50%. Introduced April 6, 2005; referred to Committee on Finance.

S. 732 (Inhofe)/H.R. 3 (Young)

Transportation Equity Act. Section 1208 on High-Occupancy Vehicle (HOV) Lanes includes provisions for alternative-fueled vehicles and energy-efficient vehicles. Section 3009 on Clean Fuels Formula Grant Program includes provisions for biodiesel, alcohol fuels, and fuel cells. Section 5213 on Metropolitan Planning directs that goals include energy conservation. Other provisions in the bill address traffic congestion, intelligent transportation systems, bicycling and pedestrian issues, and advanced vehicle technologies. House bill introduced February 9, 2005; referred to Committee on Transportation and Infrastructure. Reported (H.Rept. 109-12, Parts I and II) March 8. Passed House, amended, March 10. Senate bill reported (S.Rept. 109-53) April 6. In lieu of S. 732, Senate passed its version of H.R. 3, amended, May 17. House and Senate conferees appointed May 26.

S. 745 (Byrd)

International Clean Energy Deployment and Global Energy Markets Investment Act of 2005. Amends the Global Environmental Protection Assistance Act of 1989 to promote clean energy technology deployment in developing countries. Directs the President to establish a Task Force on International Clean Energy Cooperation. Requires the Task Force to establish an Interagency Working Group on Clean Energy Technology Exports. Establishes an Interagency Center in the Office of International Energy Market Development of the Department of Energy to assist the Working Group. Requires the Task Force to develop and submit to the President (who shall submit to Congress) a Strategy to (1) support programs and policies in developing countries that promote clean energy and energy efficiency technologies; (2) open and expand clean energy technology markets and facilitate related exports to developing countries; (3) integrate the promotion of clean energy technology deployment and greenhouse gas emissions reduction in developing countries into U.S. foreign policy objectives; (4) establish a pilot program that provides financial assistance for qualifying projects; and (5) develop financial mechanisms and instruments that are cost-effective and facilitate private capital investment in such technologies. Authorizes the Secretary of State to provide assistance to developing countries for activities consistent with the priorities established in the Strategy. Requires the ·Secretary to establish a pilot program that provides financial assistance for qualifying projects consistent with the Strategy and the performance criteria set forth in this act. Requires host country contributions. Introduced April 11, 2005; referred to Committee on Foreign Relations.

S. 808 (Durbin)

Conserve by Bicycling Program. Directs Department of Transportation (DOT) to establish at least 10 pilot bicycling projects, cost-shared with state and local governments, to demonstrate energy saving potential and other benefits. Introduced April 14, 2005; referred to Committee on Commerce, Science, and Transportation.

S. 836 (Cantwell)/H.R. 1103 (N. Johnson)

Fuel Economy Truth in Labeling Act of 2005. Directs the Administrator of the Environmental Protection Agency (EPA) to revise certain Federal vehicle fuel economy test procedures to take into consideration higher speed limits, faster acceleration rates, variations in temperature, use of air conditioning, shorter city test cycle lengths, and the use of other fuel depleting features. Senate bill introduced April 14, 2005; referred to Committee on Commerce, Science, and Transportation. House bill introduced March 3, 2005; referred to Committee on Energy and Commerce. Incorporated into H.R. 6 as floor amendment H.Amdt. 74 (as amended by H.Amdt. 75).

S. 881 (Cantwell)/H.R. 1797 (McMorris)

Spokane Tribe of Indians of the Spokane Reservation Grand Coulee Dam Equitable Compensation Settlement Act. Establishes in the Treasury the Spokane Tribe of Indians Settlement Fund. Requires the payment of compensation to the Spokane Business Council for the use of tribal lands for the generation of hydropower from the Grand Coulee Dam. Requires the use of such funds, in part, for a Cultural Resource Repository and Interpretive Center concerning the culture and history of the Spokane Tribe. Directs the Administrator of the Bonneville Power Administration to make specified settlement payments to the Spokane Tribe. Allows payments made to the Spokane Business Council or Spokane Tribe to be used or invested by the

Business Council in the same manner and for the same purposes as other Spokane Tribal governmental funds. Directs the Secretary of the Interior to transfer administrative jurisdiction from the Bureau of Reclamation to the Bureau of Indian Affairs over certain land located within the exterior boundaries of the Spokane Indian Reservation and certain other land located on the south bank of the Spokane River. Provides that payments by the Secretary and the Administrator and restoration of ownership of land in trust constitute full satisfaction of the claim of the Spokane Tribe to a fair share of the annual hydropower revenues generated by the Grand Coulee Dam project for the past and continued use of land of the Spokane Tribe for the production of hydropower at Grand Coulee Dam. House bill introduced April 21, 2005; referred to Committee on Resources. Ordered reported May 18. Senate bill introduced April 21, 2005; referred to Committee on Indian Affairs.

S. 883 (Hagel)

Climate Change Technology Deployment in Developing Countries Act of 2005. Directs the Department of State to lead an interagency effort to study and assist in reducing greenhouse gas emission intensity in developing countries. Cogeneration, renewables, and "low emission transportation" technologies are included. There is a focus on supporting U.S. technology exports and on creating demonstration projects in at least 10 countries. Introduced April 21, 2005; referred to Committee on Foreign Relations.

S. 887 (Hagel)

Climate Change Technology Deployment and Infrastructure Credit Act of 2005. Directs the Secretary of Energy to carry out activities that promote the adoption of technologies that reduce greenhouse gas intensity and to provide credit-based financial assistance and investment protection for projects that employ advanced climate technologies or systems, and for other purposes. Includes renewable energy demonstration projects and financial incentives for energy efficiency. Introduced April 21, 2005; referred to Committee on Energy and Natural Resources.

S. 889 (Feinstein)/H.R. 705 (Gilchrest)

Automobile Fuel Economy Act of 2005. Sets forth certain increased average fuel economy standards for certain light trucks, automobiles (up to 10,000 pounds gross vehicle weight), and certain classes of vehicles in the federal fleet that are manufactured or purchased after specified dates. Senate bill introduced April 21, 2005; referred to Committee on Commerce,

Science, and Transportation. House bill introduced February 9, 2005; referred to Committee on Energy and Commerce and Committee on Government Reform.

S. 890 (Sarbanes)

Transit in Parks Act. Provides for development of alternative transportation in certain federally owned or managed areas that are open to the general public. Introduced April 22, 2005; referred to Committee on Energy and Natural Resources.

S. 918 (Obama)

Provides for Flexible Fuel Vehicle (FFV) refueling capability at new and existing refueling station facilities to promote energy security and reduction of greenhouse gas emissions. Introduced April 27, 2005; referred to Committee on Finance.

S. 962 (Grassley)

Clean Energy Bonds Act of 2005. Establishes a tax credit to holders of qualified bonds issued to finance renewable energy projects. The bond would be available to 'non-profit utilities," including electric cooperatives, public power systems, and municipal utilities. When a non-profit utility issues a clean energy bond, the federal government pays a tax credit to the bondholder instead of the issuer paying interest. The credit would be set at a value so there is zero interest cost to the issuer. Technologies that are eligible for the renewable energy production tax credit (PTC) would be eligible for the bond. Introduced April 28, 2005; referred to Committee on Finance.

S. 971 (Hatch)

Clean Efficient Automobiles Resulting From Advanced Car Technologies (CLEAR ACT) Act of 2005. Creates a tax credit for investment in alternative motor vehicles, including qualified fuel cell, hybrid, and alternative fuel vehicles. Bases the amount of such credit on criteria relating to vehicle weight and fuel efficiency. Modifies the tax credit for qualified electric vehicles to remove the 10% limitation and base the credit amount on criteria relating to vehicle weight, mileage, and payload. Makes leased vehicles eligible for such credit. Extends such credit through 2010. Allows a tax credit for (1) 50 percent of expenditures for the installation of qualified clean-fuel vehicle refueling property; and (2) retail sales of alternative fuels as motor vehicle fuels. Directs the Comptroller General to undertake an ongoing analysis of the effectiveness of the alternative motor vehicle and fuel incentives provided by this act and to report to Congress on such study by December 31, 2006, and annually thereafter. Introduced April 28, 2005; referred to Committee on Finance.

S. 1022 (Smith)

Resource Efficient Appliance Incentives Act of 2005. Establishes a business tax credit for the production of certain water and energy efficient appliances (e.g., dishwashers, clothes washers, and refrigerators). Bases the amount of such credit on specified energy and water efficiency ratings. Introduced May 12, 2005; referred to Committee on Finance.

S. 1042 (Warner)/H.R. 1815 (Hunter)

National Defense Authorization Act for FY2006. Section 2402 authorizes funding for energy conservation projects. House bill introduced April 26, 2005; referred to Committee on Armed Services. Includes $50 million authorization. Reported (H.Rept. 109-89) May 20. Passed House May 25. Senate bill introduced May 12, 2005; referred to Committee on Armed Services. Includes $60 million authorization. Reported (S.Rept. 109-69) May 17.

S. 1076 (Lincoln)/H.R. 2498 (Hulshof)

Extends through December 31, 2010, the tax credit for biodiesel used as fuel and the excise credits for biodiesel mixtures and biodiesel used to produce biodiesel mixtures. House bill introduced May 19, 2005; referred to Committee on Ways and Means. Senate bill introduced May 19, 2005; referred to Committee on Finance.

S. 1077 (Lincoln)

Establishes renewable liquid fuels tax credits. Section 1 establishes a 1.00 per gallon five-year excise tax credit, through December 31, 2010. Section 2 establishes a $1.00 per gallon income tax credit for five years, through December 31, 2010. Introduced May 19, 2005; referred to Committee on Finance.

S. 1078 (Lincoln)

Landfill Gas-to-Energy Tax Credit Act. Section 2 extends the renewable energy production tax credit (PTC) for trash combustion facilities for three years, through December 31, 2008. Also, Section 3 changes the application of the tax credit for nonconventional ("Section 29") fuels. Introduced May 19, 2005; referred to Committee on Finance.

S. 1079 (Lincoln)

Waste-to-Energy Tax Credit Act. Extends the renewable energy production tax credit (PTC) for trash combustion facilities for three years, through December 31, 2008. Also, it changes the eligibility period from 10 years to seven. Introduced May 19, 2005; referred to Committee on Finance.

S. 1093 (Salazar)

Research and Development Investment Act. Section 2 authorizes $20 million per year through 2025 for the Renewable Energy Production Incentive (REPI). Section 3 extends the PTC for five years, through December 31, 2011. Section 4 provides a 10% investment tax credit for residential solar and geothermal equipment. Section 5 delays the phase-out of the tax incentives for qualified electric vehicles for one year. Reauthorizes and revises the Renewable Energy Production Incentive (REPI) program. Introduced May 20, 2005; referred to Committee on Finance.

S. 1151 (McCain)

Climate Stewardship and Innovation Act of 2005. Creates a market-driven system of greenhouse gas tradeable allowances to support deployment of new climate change-related technologies. Includes provisions for energy efficiency audits (Section 545), deployment of biofuels and solar technologies (Section 471), and reverse auctions for renewable electricity and energy efficiency (Section 491). Introduced May 26, 2005; referred to Committee on Environment and Public Works.

S. 1156 (Hatch)

Section 1(a) sets a five-year eligibility period for certain open-loop biomass facilities covered by the renewable energy production tax credit (PTC). Also, Section 1(b) extends the PTC for two years, through December 31, 2007. Introduced May 26, 2005; referred to Committee on Finance.

S. 1203 (Hagel)

Climate Change Technology Tax Incentives Act of 2005. Provides tax incentives for the investment in greenhouse gas intensity reduction projects. Introduced June 8, 2005; referred to Committee on Finance.

S. 1208 (Alexander)

Environmentally Responsible Windpower Act of 2005. Provides for local control over the siting of wind machines, including prohibiting federal subsidies for machines located within 20 miles of national monuments.

Introduced June 9, 2005; referred to Committee on Energy and Natural Resources.

S. 1210 (Harkin)

National Security and Bioenergy Investment Act of 2005. Provides for research, development, demonstration, administrative support, and market mechanisms for widespread deployment and commercialization of biobased fuels and biobased products. Introduced June 9, 2005; referred to Committee on Agriculture, Nutrition, and Forestry.

CONGRESSIONAL HEARINGS, REPORTS, AND DOCUMENTS

U.S. Congress. House. Committee on Energy and Commerce. *Full Committee Markup of the Energy Policy Act of 2005.* Markup held April 5 and 6, 2005. [http://energycommerce.house.gov/108/Markups/04062005markup1473.htm]

U.S. Congress. House. Committee on Energy and Commerce. *Committee Print of the Energy Policy Act of 2005.* Posted April 5, 2005. [http://energycommerce.house.gov/108/energy_pdfs_2.htm]

U.S. Congress. Senate. Committee on Appropriations. Subcommittee on Energy and Water. *FY2006 Budget Request for the DOE Office of Energy Efficiency and Renewable Energy (EERE) and other DOE Offices.* Hearing held March 15, 2005. [http://appropriations.senate.gov/hearmarkups/record.cfm?id=233443]

U.S. Congress. House. Committee on Appropriations. Subcommittee on Energy and Water Development, and Related Agencies. *Department of Energy —[FY2006 Budget Request for] Science, Nuclear Energy, and Renewable Energy.*
Hearing held March 15, 2005.
[No hearing webcast has been posted to the web and no testimony has been published yet.]

U.S. Congress. Joint Committee on Taxation. *Description and Analysis of Certain Federal Tax Provisions Expiring in 2005 and 2006.* Report JCX-12-05. March 11, 2005. Part IIB of the report has a section (p. 51-60) on the renewable energy production tax credit (PTC) entitled the "Credit for electricity produced from certain renewable resources." Also, Part IIA has a section (p. 20-34) on the research and experimentation (R&E) tax credit. [http://www.house.gov/jct /pubs05.html]

U.S. Congress. Senate. Committee on Energy and Natural Resources. *Power Generation Resource Incentives & Diversity Standards.* Hearing held March 8, 2005. [http://energy.senate.gov/hearings/witnesslist.cfm?id =1403]

U.S. Congress. Senate. Committee on Energy and Natural Resources. *Department of Energy Budget.* Hearing held March 3, 2005. [http:// energy.senate.gov/hearings/witnesslist.cfm?id=1370]

U.S. Congress. House. Committee on Energy and Commerce. Subcommittee on Energy and Air Quality. *The Energy Policy Act of 2005: Ensuring Jobs for Our Future with Secure and Reliable Energy.* Hearings held February 9, 10, and 16, 2005. [http://energycommerce. house.gov/108/Hearings/02102005hearing1428/hearing.htm]

U.S. Congress. House. Committee on Science. Improving the Nation's Energy Security: Can Cars and Trucks Be Made More Fuel Efficient? Hearing held February 9, 2005. [http://www.house.gov/science/hearings/ full05/feb9/February92005.htm]

(Many hearings on Energy Efficiency and Renewable Energy held in the 108th Congress are listed on the DOE Office of Energy Efficiency and Renewable Energy website at [http://www.eere.energy.gov/office_eere /congressional_test.html].)

In: Energy Efficiency   ISBN: 1-59454-684-3
Editor: Lara S. Zambini, pp. 41-62   © 2006 Nova Science Publishers, Inc.

Chapter 2

ENERGY EFFICIENCY: BUDGET, OIL CONSERVATION, AND ELECTRICITY CONSERVATION ISSUES [*]

Fred Sissine

SUMMARY

Energy security, a major driver of federal energy efficiency programs in the past, came back into play as oil and gas prices rose late in the year 2000. The terrorist attack in 2001 and the Iraq war have led to heightened concern for energy security and raised further concerns about the vulnerability of energy infrastructure and the need for alternative fuels. Further, the 2001 power shortages in California, the 2003 northeast-midwest power blackout, and continuing high natural gas and oil prices have brought a renewed emphasis on energy efficiency and energy conservation to dampen electricity, oil, and natural gas demand.

Also, worldwide emphasis on environmental problems of air and water pollution and global climate change, the related development of clean energy technologies in western Europe and Japan, and technology competitiveness may remain important influences on energy efficiency policymaking.

The Bush Administration's FY2006 budget request for the Department of Energy's (DOE's) Energy Efficiency Program seeks $846.8 million, $21.4

---

[*] Excerpted from CRS Report Order Code IB10020 dated June 17, 2005

million less than FY2005. This includes $575.8 million for R&D and $271.0 million for grants.

The House passed H.R. 2419, the Energy and Water (E&W) appropriations bill for FY2006, which funds DOE's Energy Efficiency (Conservation) and Renewable Energy programs. A new account structure does not provide a total figure for energy efficiency programs.

The House has passed H.R. 6, the Energy Policy Act of 2005, with many non-tax energy efficiency provisions similar to H.R. 6 of the 108th Congress. It reauthorizes many pro grams, sets a new goal for reducing federal facilities energy use, extends federal Energy Saving Performance Contracts (ESPCs), establishes several standards for products equipment, and could terminate cogeneration purchase requirements. Further, it has $0.4 billion in tax incentives for energy efficiency.

The Senate version of H.R. 6 (incorporates S. 10) is on the Senate floor. Thus the main differences from the House bill stronger standards for products and equipment (§135 and §136) and a major oil savings provision (§151). Also, the tax package in Senate Finance Committee has about $5. billion in tax incentives for energy efficiency, including $3.7 billion for equipment and $1. billion for vehicles.

In the 108th Congress, the conference version of the omnibus energy bill (H.R. had significant tax and regulatory measures for energy efficiency. It would have allowed DOE to set an efficiency standard for "standby mode" energy use in battery chargers external power supplies; set equipment efficiency standards by statute and rule; and set higher goal for efficiency in federal facilities The bill did not pass, in part due to concerns about cost and the controversial MTBE harbor" provision.

P.L. 108-357 provided tax-exempt bonds for green buildings and reduced the tax deduction for SUVs. P.L. 108-311 extended a credit for electric vehicles and a tax deduction for clean fuel vehicles. Neither law contained any of the key energy efficiency tax provisions in H.R. 6, S. 2095, or S. 1637.

MOST RECENT DEVELOPMENTS

A June 16 draft Senate amendment to H.R. 6, entitled "Climate and Economy Insurance Act," would create (§1526) a Climate Change Trust Fund with incentives for energy efficiency and conservation. Also on June 16, the Senate adopted S.Amdt. 775, incorporating S. 10 into its version of H.R. 6, which is on the Senate floor. Further, the Senate Finance Committee chairman's mark for tax provisions to be incorporated into the Senate bill has $5.4 billion (29%) for efficiency, with $3.7 billion for equipment and $1.7 billion for vehicles. On May 26, 2005, the Senate Energy and Natural Resources Committee reported S. 10 with several non-tax energy efficiency provisions. The House-passed version of H.R. 6, the Energy Policy Act of 2005, contains many non-tax energy efficiency provisions similar to those of H.R. 6 in the 108th Congress. It has about $0.4 billion in tax incentives for efficiency and conservation. (Key issues of H.R. 6 are described in CRS Issue Brief IB10143, *Energy Policy: Comprehensive Energy Legislation (H.R. 6) in the 109th Congress*; the renewable energy provisions in H.R. 6 and other bills of the 109th Congress are discussed in "Energy Efficiency in the 109th Congress," below; and the provisions in H.R. 6 and S. 2095 from the 108th Congress are described in "Energy Efficiency in 108th Congress Omnibus Energy Bills," below.)

On June 16, the Senate Appropriations Committee reported the FY2006 Energy and Water Appropriations bill (H.R. 2419), which provides funding for DOE's Energy Efficiency (Conservation) and Renewable Energy programs. Compared with the House-passed bill, the Senate version of H.R 2419 has increases of $32 million for Vehicle Technologies and $5 million for Weatherization, and it has decreases of $15 million for Program Direction, and $2.4 million for Industrial Technologies. (For more details, see "DOE Budget, FY2006," and **Table 3**.) The FY2006 request for EPA's Climate Protection (Energy Efficiency) Programs is $113.3 million, which is $3.8 million higher than the FY2005 request. (For more details, see "EPA Budget, FY2006," and **Table 2**.)

BACKGROUND AND ANALYSIS

Energy Efficiency Concept

Energy efficiency is increased when an energy conversion device, such as a household appliance, automobile engine, or steam turbine, undergoes a technical change that enables it to provide the same service (lighting, heating, motor drive) while using less energy. The energy-saving result of the efficiency improvement is often called "energy conservation." The energy efficiency of buildings can be improved through the use of certain materials such as attic insulation, components such as insulated windows, and design aspects such as solar orientation and shade tree landscaping. Further, the energy efficiency of communities and cities can be improved through architectural design, transportation system design, and land use planning. Thus, energy efficiency involves all aspects of energy production, distribution, and end-use.

> These ideas of "efficiency" and "conservation" contrast with "curtailment," which decreases output (e.g., turning down the thermostat) or services (e.g., driving less) to curb energy use. That is, energy curtailment occurs when saving energy causes a reduction in services or sacrifice of comfort. Curtailment is often employed as an emergency measure.

Energy efficiency is often viewed as a resource option like coal, oil, or natural gas. In contrast to supply options, however, the downward pressure on energy prices created by energy efficiency comes from demand reductions instead of increased supply. As a result, energy efficiency can reduce resource use and environmental impacts.

History

From 1974 through 1992, Congress established several complementary programs, primarily at the Department of Energy (DOE), to implement energy saving measures in virtually every sector of societal activity. These energy efficiency and energy conservation programs were created originally in response to national oil import security and economic stability concerns. In the early 1980s, states and utilities took an active role in promoting energy efficiency as a cost-saving "demand-side management" tool for avoiding expensive powerplant construction. Since 1988, national interest in energy efficiency has focused increasingly on energy efficiency as a tool for mitigating environmental problems such as air pollution and global climate change. This aspect spawned new programs at DOE and at several other agencies, including the Environmental Protection Agency (EPA), the Agency for International Development (AID), and the World Bank's Global Environment Facility (GEF). Energy efficiency is increasingly viewed as a critical element of sustainable development and economic growth.

The DOE energy efficiency program includes R&D funding, grants to state and local governments, and a regulatory framework of appliance efficiency standards and voluntary guidelines for energy-efficient design in buildings. In addition, its budget supports regulatory programs for energy efficiency goals in federal agencies and standards for consumer products. (Detailed descriptions of DOE programs appear in DOE's *FY2006*

Congressional Budget Request, DOE/ME-0052, vol. 7, February 2005, available at [http://www.cfo.doe.gov/budget/06budget/Start.htm].)

From FY1973 through FY2002, DOE spent about $11.7 billion in 2003 constant dollars for energy efficiency R&D, which amounts to about 9% of the total federal spending for energy supply R&D during that period. In 2003 constant (real) dollars, energy efficiency R&D funding declined from $795 million in FY1979 to $227 million in FY1988 and then climbed to $556 million in FY1994. For FY2003, $612 million was appropriated, which was $56 million, or 9%, above the FY1994 mark in 2003 constant dollars. Also, in 2003 constant dollars, since FY1973, DOE has spent about $7.7 billion on grants for state and local conservation programs.

This spending history can be viewed within the context of DOE spending for the three major energy supply R&D programs: nuclear, fossil, and renewable energy R&D. From FY1948 through FY1972, in 2003 constant dollars, the federal government spent about $24.3 billion for nuclear (fission and fusion) R&D and about $5.5 billion for fossil energy R&D. From FY1973 through FY2003, the federal government spent $49.1 billion for nuclear (fission and fusion), $24.8 billion for fossil, $14.6 billion for renewables, and $11.7 billion for energy efficiency. Total energy R&D spending from FY1948 to FY1998, in 2003 constant dollars, reached $131.2 billion, including $74.0 billion, or 56%, for nuclear, $30.9 billion, or 24%, for fossil, $14.6 billion, or 11%, for renewables, and $11.7 billion, or 9%, for energy efficiency.

DOE's FY2004 energy efficiency R&D funding totaled $559.7 million, or about 24% of DOE's energy R&D appropriation. Renewable energy R&D received $439.4 million (19%), fossil energy received $672.8 million (29%), and fission and fusion were appropriated $667.4 million (29%).

Since 1985, national energy use has climbed about 20 Q (quads — quadrillion Btus, British thermal units), reaching a record high of 99 Q in 2000. DOE's 1995 report *Energy Conservation Trends* found that energy efficiency and conservation activities from 1973 through 1991 curbed the pre-1973 growth trend in annual primary energy use by about 18 Q, an 18% reduction. In 1992, this was saving the economy about $150 billion annually in total U.S. energy expenditures, a one-fourth reduction from the previous trend.

DOE's Strategic and Performance Goals

In 2004, a National Academy of Public Administration (NAPA) study found dramatic improvement in the Office of Energy Efficiency and Renewable Energy (EERE) after a major reorganization that included new offices for FreedomCAR and Vehicle Technologies and for Hydrogen, Fuel Cells, and Infrastructure. Information about the new management structure and other aspects of EERE are available on the DOE website at [http://www.eere.energy.gov/office_eere/]. The study is available on the NAPA website at [http://www.napawash.org/Pubs/EERE%20NAPA %20Rpt%20Sept%2004.htm].

A National Research Council report, *Energy Research at DOE: Was it Worth It?*, found that from 1978 to 2000 an investment of about $8 billion in DOE's Energy Efficiency Programs produced an economic return of at least $30 billion. Areas found short of expected benefits lacked incentives needed for private-sector adoption.

A 2004 Resources for the Future (RFF) report, *The Effectiveness and Cost of Energy Efficiency Programs*, reviews a broad range of studies about DOE and EPA programs. The report estimates that a selected range of non-transportation programs saves four Q of energy per year and estimates carbon and air pollution emission savings. The full report is available on the RFF website at [http://www.rff.org/Documents/RFF-DP-04-19REV.pdf].

The President's Management Agenda set out the Bush Administration's framework for performance management based on human capital, competitive sourcing, financial performance, electronic government, and integration of budget with performance. The Government Performance and Results Act (GPRA, P.L. 103-62) requires each federal agency to produce and update a strategic plan linked to annual performance plans.

In DOE's *Strategic Plan of September 2000*, energy efficiency objectives and strategies appear under strategic goal #1, "Energy Resources." In the *DOE Annual Performance Plan (APP) for FY2004*, energy efficiency is addressed under the revised strategic goal #2, "Energy Conservation and the Environment," which states: "Energy use and greenhouse gas emissions versus the gross domestic product (GDP) are reduced by 40% by 2025 compared to 2000 and the growth versus the U.S. population stops by 2025." In support of Goal 2, the APP lists five strategic performance goals. ER1-1 says that relative to the 1985 baseline, DOE's Federal Energy Management Program (FEMP) will support federal agency efforts to reduce energy intensity by 30% in 2005 and 35% by 2010. ER 1-2 says that from 1991 to 2010, the Industries Program will reduce energy intensity by 20-25%. ER 1-

3 says the FreedomCAR and Vehicle Technologies Program will achieve several specific vehicle technical and cost goals through 2010. ER 1-4 says that the Buildings Program will achieve several specific goals to improve building efficiency through 2009. ER 3-1 puts forth specific output goals through 2010 for weatherization grants, state grants, Rebuild America, Energy Star, Clean Cities, and for other programs.

Energy Efficiency in the 109th Congress

Efficiency Standards for Consumer and Commercial Products

DOE currently sets minimum energy efficiency standards for several consumer and commercial products, including household appliances such as clothes washers and refrigerators. H.R. 6 (§133) would authorize the DOE Secretary to expand efficiency standards within three years to cover "standby mode" energy use by battery chargers and external power supplies. It would also legislate efficiency standards for exit signs, torchieres, traffic signals, and distribution transformers and it calls for DOE to set standards by rule for suspended ceiling fans, vending machines, unit heaters, and commercial refrigerators and freezers. H.R. 6 in the 108th Congress had identical provisions for these standards. In testimony (March 2003) on H.R. 6 in the 108th Congress, the American Council for an Energy-Efficient Economy estimated that these new standards would save more energy than any other efficiency provisions in the bill. The table below indicates which standards would be set by law and which would be set by DOE rulemaking.

Standard set:	H.R. 6 (House-passed)
By law	exit signs, traffic signals, torchieres, distribution transformers, unit heaters, medium base compact fluorescent lamps
By rule	ceiling fans, vending machines, commercial refrigerators and freezers and refrigerator-freezers, residential furnace fans

Efficiency Goals for Federal Buildings

The purpose of federal efficiency goals is to lead by example in saving energy, reducing costs, and helping transform markets for new equipment. The past goal had called for a 20% reduction in federal buildings' energy use, measured in energy use per square foot (sf), from 1985 to 2000. This goal was exceeded, slightly. H.R. 6 (§102) would set a goal for further energy efficiency in federal facilities. Compared to the baseline year energy use in 2003, the goal is a 20% energy reduction over a 10-year period from

2006 to 2015. Also, DOE is required to review results by the end of the 10-year period and recommend further goals for an additional decade. Most of the other provisions for federal programs are administrative measures that would help agencies achieve the above-described goal.

The historical record shows that congressional buildings have had less focus on energy efficiency goals than those in the executive branch. To address this, H.R. 6 (§101) calls for the implementation of a plan for congressional buildings to meet the energy efficiency goal for federal agencies noted above. It also calls for a study of the potential for energy efficiency and renewables to increase reliability during a power outage and authorizes up to $2 million annually, over five years.

Tax Incentives for Efficiency and Conservation

Since the late 1970s, there have been some tax incentives to promote fuel switching and alternative fuels as a way to conserve gasoline and reduce oil import dependence. In contrast, tax incentives for energy efficiency and for electricity conservation have been rare, and generally short-lived. H.R. 6 proposes two modest new tax credits for energy efficiency. Section 1312 encourages business use of fuel cells and Section 1317 aims to improve efficiency in existing homes.

Energy Efficiency Tax Revenue Effect. Table 1, below, compares the estimated 10-year revenue effect of energy efficiency and conservation tax provisions in the House-passed version of H.R. 6, and the Senate Finance Committee chairman's mark.

Table 1. H.R. 6, Tax Revenue Effect
($ billions)

	House	Sen. Finance Cmte.
Energy Efficiency and Conservation Measures (§1312 and §1317 in House bill, excluding diesel fuels, alternative fuels, and solar credit)	$0.397	$3.733
Hybrid and Fuel Cell Vehicles	——	$1.686
Total, Energy Efficiency and Conservation	$0.397	$5.419
Gross Total, All Tax Provisions	$8.090	$18.421
Energy Efficiency and Conservation Share of Total	4.9%	29.4%

Source: Joint Committee on Taxation (JCT), Estimated Revenue Effects of the Chairman's Amendment in the Nature of a Substitute to H.R. 1541, Scheduled for Markup by the Committee on Ways and Means, April 13, 2005 (JCX-17-05); Estimated Revenue Effects of the Chairman's Amendment in the Nature of a Substitute to the "Energy Policy Tax Incentives Act of 2005," Scheduled for Markup by the Committee on Finance, June 16, 2005 (JCX-47-05).

Housing, Funding Authorizations, and Other Provisions

H.R. 6 has several provisions (§ 141-149) for energy efficiency in public housing. Also, Section 121 authorizes funding for energy assistance (e.g., Low-Income Home Energy Assistance Program, LIHEAP), and Sections 122 and 123 authorizes grant programs (e.g., DOE Weatherization Program and State Energy Program). Several other energy efficiency programs are authorized in Title I and Title IX.

Energy Efficiency in 108th Congress Omnibus Energy Bills

In the 108th Congress, most legislative action on energy efficiency focused on omnibus energy policy bills, S. 1637, S. 2095, H.R. 6, and S. 14/S. 1149. Late in 2003, a cloture motion to stop a Senate filibuster on the conference report (H.Rept. 108-375) for H.R. 6 failed (57-40). Key objections cited in Senate debate included budget concerns and the Title XV "safe harbor" from product liability lawsuits for producers of MTBE (methyl tertiary-butyl ether), ethanol, and other renewable fuels.

Several significant energy efficiency provisions were included in S. 1637, S. 2095, and H.R. 6. Key provisions included proposals that would have required a DOE rulemaking to set an efficiency standard for "standby mode" energy use in battery chargers and external power supplies; legislated standards for certain equipment and directed DOE to set a standard by rule for other types of equipment; and set goals for efficiency in federal buildings. Other provisions would have created incentives for energy efficiency measures in home construction, home renovation, appliances, residential equipment, commercial buildings, fuel cells, and combined heat and power equipment, and for alternative fuels. (For a detailed summary of provisions in the conference version of H.R. 6, see CRS Report RL32204, and see CRS Report RL32078, which compares House and Senate versions of H.R. 6 with S. 14. For side-by-side comparisons of provisions in H.R. 6, see CRS Report RL32033 (non-tax provisions), CRS Report RL32042 (tax provisions), and CRS Report RL32041 (electricity provisions).

DOE Budget, FY2006

The Department of Energy (DOE) request seeks $846.8 million for energy efficiency, which is $21.4 million, or 2%, less than the FY2005 appropriation (excluding inflation). The main increases are for

Biofuels/Biorefinery ($14.5 million) and Fuel Cells ($8.7 million). The main cuts are for Industrial programs (-$18.3 million), Advanced Combustion Vehicles (-$8.7 million), Buildings (-$7.5 million), Clean Cities (-$4.1 million), and State Energy Program (-$3.2 million).

The FY2006 budget request (Appendix, p. 402) notes that the "Administration's energy efficiency programs have the potential to produce substantial benefits for the nation — both now and in the future — in terms of economic growth, increased energy security and a cleaner environment." In particular, the request aims to "accelerate" the development of hydrogen-powered fuel cell vehicles. The Hydrogen program aims to facilitate industry commercialization of infrastructure for those vehicles by 2015. Goals for other energy end-use and production technologies generally seek to improve energy efficiency and performance while reducing costs. The request also proposes funding tax credits, including an investment tax credit for combined heat and power (CHP) through the end of 2009, an extension of the hybrid vehicle tax credit through the end of 2008, and a tax credit for fuel cell vehicles purchased through the end of 2012.

EPA Budget, FY2006

The FY2006 request for EPA's Climate Protection Programs (CPPs) is $113.3 million, which is $3.8 million more than FY2005 request. This includes $3.6 million more under the Office of Environmental Programs and Management (EPM) and $0.3 million more under the Office of Science and Technology (S&T).

EPA conducts its CPP programs under the Office of Atmospheric Programs, with funding from appropriation accounts for EPM and S&T. EPM programs cover the areas of buildings, industry, state and local government, international, and sequestration. S&T programs mainly cover transportation. CPP programs focus mainly on voluntary energy efficiency activities. These programs include Green Lights, Energy Star Buildings, Energy Star Products, Climate Wise, and Transportation Partners. They involve public-private partnerships that promote energy-efficient lighting, buildings, and office equipment. Efforts also include labeling, information dissemination, and other activities to overcome market barriers.

**Table 2. EPA Funding for Climate Protection
Energy Efficiency Programs (CPP)
($ millions current)**

	FY2004 Enacted	FY2005 Request	FY2006 Request	FY2006 -FY2005	Percent Diff.
Environ. Programs & Management	88.5	92.0	95.5	3.6	4%
Science & Technology	21.8	17.5	17.7	0.3	2%
TOTAL	110.3	109.4	113.3	3.8	3%

Source: EPA FY2006 Congressional Justification of Appropriation Estimates (EPA-205/R-05-001), Feb. 2005, [http://www.epa.gov/ocfo], pp. S&T-6, EPM-29, Appendix-75.

Energy Security

The September 11, 2001, terrorist attacks focused national attention on developing a strategy to address the vulnerabilities of energy systems and other essential services. The Department of Homeland Security (DHS, P.L. 107-296) includes offices and programs (Infrastructure Protection, Energy Security and Assurance) responsible for measures to protect energy infrastructure, including power plants, transmission lines, oil refineries, oil storage tanks, oil and natural gas pipelines, and other energy infrastructure. By reducing the demand for fuels and electricity, energy efficiency measures may contribute to energy security by slowing growth in the number of energy facilities and amount of other energy infrastructure. It can also reduce the risk of oil shortages, energy price shocks, and attendant impacts on the national economy. Some of the possible ways that energy efficiency can improve energy security are described in DOE's report *Homeland Security: Safeguarding America's Future with Energy Efficiency and Renewable Energy Technologies* and in *U.S. Energy Security Facts* (available at [http://www.rmi.org/images/other/EnergySecurity/S03-04_USESFtext.pdf]).

Electricity Demand-Side Management (DSM) and Distributed Power

The August 2003 electric power blackout that affected several states and Canadian provinces rekindled interest in energy efficiency, energy conservation/demand response measures, and distributed power generation. The use of energy-efficient appliances and other end-use equipment can reduce electricity demand, which drives the need for new power plants. Further, the development of small, modular "distributed energy" systems (also referred to as distributed generation and distributed power) under

DOE's program may help reduce the security risk by decentralizing energy facilities and establishing some facilities off-grid. Also, the "response and recovery" element in the President's DHS proposal called for it to "ensure rapid restoration of transportation systems, energy production, transmission, and distribution systems...." The deployment of smaller, highly mobile distributed energy equipment may help address this aspect of energy security. H.R. 6 has provisions (§126, §932) for distributed energy. (For more on distributed energy, see the DOE website at [http://www. eere.energy.gov/EE/power_distributed_generation.html] and at [http://www. eere.energy.gov/distributedpower/].)

Energy Conservation to Curb Natural Gas Demand

The Secretary of Energy requested that the National Petroleum Council (NPC) report on policy options to address the problem of high natural gas prices. The report, *Balancing Natural Gas Policy,* says gas prices could average from $5 to $7 per thousand cubic feet for years to come, and it concludes, among other options, that energy conservation and greater energy efficiency have the biggest immediate potential to hold down prices. The report recommends updating building codes and equipment standards, promoting Energy Star equipment, using the most efficient power plants, deploying distributed energy, installing smart controls, and employing best practices for low-income weatherization. The Alliance to Save Energy and the American Council for an Energy-Efficient Economy (ACEEE) applaud the NPC recommendations but stress that many other measures — including tax incentives, utility performance standards, federal buildings improvements, and regulations to make energy conservation profitable for utilities — were not in the report and should be considered. Also, a 2005 report by ACEEE, *Impacts of Energy Efficiency and Renewable Energy on Natural Gas Markets: Updated and Expanded Analysis,* says that in one year, a massive energy efficiency effort could be put in place that would reduce gas use by 1% and cut prices by 37%. (The NPC report is at [http://www.npc.org/] and the ACEEE report is at [http://www.aceee. org/press/0504eerespond.html].)

On January 24, 2005, the Senate Energy and Natural Resources Committee held a natural gas conference. Some participants described the potential for energy efficiency to reduce gas demand and prices. See [http://energy.senate.gov/conference/conference.cfm]. Some statements refer to a recent DOE study, *Easing the Natural Gas Crisis: Reducing Natural Gas Prices through Increased Deployment of Renewable Energy and Energy Efficiency,* available at [http://eetd.lbl.gov/ea/ems/reports/56756.pdf].

Vehicle Fuel Efficiency and Oil Conservation

Energy efficiency measures to curb oil demand, and other oil conservation measures, may help address energy security, economic issues such as high gasoline prices and oil import dependence, and environmental issues such as air pollution, climate change, and the proposal to develop oil in the Arctic National Wildlife Refuge (ANWR).

For the ANWR issue, technology-driven improvements to the fuel economy of cars and light trucks — without any change to the Corporate Average Fuel Economy (CAFE) standard — might save more fuel than would likely be produced by oil drilling in ANWR, although the two options are not mutually exclusive. The Energy Information Administration (EIA) says that a technology-driven projection for cars and light trucks could increase fuel economy by 3.6 mpg by 2020. Through the first 20 years, this increase would generate oil savings equivalent to four times the low case and three-fourths of the high case projected for ANWR oil production. Extended through 50 years, the fuel economy savings would range from 10 times the low case to more than double the high case for ANWR. (For more information on this issue, see CRS Report RL31033, *Energy Efficiency and Renewable Energy Fuel Equivalents to Potential Oil Production from the Arctic National Wildlife Refuge*).

CAFE is a key federal regulatory policy that had instituted a gradual ramp-up of fuel efficiency for newly manufactured cars and light trucks. The present CAFE standard for new cars is 27.5 mpg. The national fleet fuel economy for cars peaked at 21.1 mpg in 1991, declined slightly, and then climbed to 22.3 mpg in 2003. Similarly, light trucks peaked at 17.4 mpg in 1993, declined slightly, and then reached 17.7 in 2003. A floor amendment (H.Amdt. 73) to H.R. 6 to raise fuel economy standards failed to pass. H.Amdt. 75 was passed, requiring EPA to revise its adjustment factors to increase the accuracy of fuel economy labels. (For more on CAFE standards, see CRS Issue Brief IB90122, *Automobile and Light Truck Fuel Economy: Is CAFE up to Standards?*)

A report by the Congressional Budget Office (CBO), *The Economic Costs of Fuel Economy Standards Versus a Gasoline Tax*, found that a 46-cent-per-gallon gasoline tax increase would achieve a 10% reduction in fuel use at a cost that is 3% less than the cost of creating a higher CAFE standard with or without credit trading.

The Bush Administration's hydrogen fuel initiative seeks to accelerate the use of fuel cells for transportation and power generation. Fuel cells can reduce gasoline (hence oil) use due to the ability to employ hydrogen-rich fuels, such as natural gas and alcohol fuels. The initiative builds on the

Administration's Freedom Cooperative Automobile Research (FreedomCAR) Program. FreedomCAR creates a partnership with the auto industry to develop a fuel-cell-powered vehicle that would attain commercial use during 2010 to 2020. This program is funded primarily by DOE's Fuel Cell Technologies Program (see **Table 3**) but includes some funding from other agencies. (For more details on FreedomCAR see CRS Report RS21442, *Hydrogen and Fuel Cell Vehicle R&D: FreedomCAR and the President's Hydrogen Fuel Initiative.*)

Oil use for gasoline, home heating, and other applications makes it important to the transportation and production sectors of the nation's economy. Thus, fluctuating oil prices and dependence on imported sources can create economic vulnerabilities. Also, oil use has important environmental impacts. Its extraction and transport can lead to spills that pollute land and water. Further, oil-based fuels, such as gasoline, generate sulphur dioxide and other air pollutants as well as large amounts of carbon dioxide that contribute to climate change.

U.S. oil use accounts for about 25% (2003) of the world's oil consumption and about 40% (2003) of total U.S. energy use. The nation uses (2003) about 20.1 million barrels of oil per day (mb/d), of which about 13.2 mb/d is used for transportation, including about 5.0 mb/d for cars and 3.7 mb/d for light trucks (includes pickups, minivans, and sport utility vehicles).

Oil use in transportation can also be reduced through short-term conservation measures such as increased use of public transit, carpooling and ridesharing, and telecommuting; and through curtailment (e.g., driving less) and substitution of alternative fuels. Other measures can help reduce non-transportation oil uses. For example, home improvement measures such as insulation, energy-efficient windows, and weatherization measures can reduce the use of home heating oil.

Climate Change: Energy Efficiency's Role

The FY2004 Foreign Operations, Export Financing, and Related Programs Appropriations Act (P.L. 108-199, Division D, Section 555) provided $180 million for "energy conservation, energy efficiency, and clean energy" to reduce greenhouse gas emissions in developing countries.

DOE's November 2003 report *U.S. Climate Change Technology Program —Technology Options for the Near and Long Term* compiles information from multiple federal agencies on more than 80 technologies. For these end-use and supply technologies, the report describes President

Bush's initiatives and R&D goals for advancing technology development, but it does not estimate emissions saving potentials, as some previous DOE reports on the topic had presented.

Energy efficiency is seen as a key means to reduce fossil fuel-induced carbon dioxide (CO_2) emissions that may contribute to global climate change. Thus, recent debates over the U.S. role in the Kyoto Protocol and related international negotiations to curb global emissions of greenhouse gases tend to be reflected in deliberations over federal funding and incentives for energy efficiency.

In fulfilling requirements under the United Nations Framework Convention on Climate Change (UNFCCC), EPA issued the third U.S. climate report to the United Nations entitled *Climate Action Report 2002*. In it, the Bush Administration commits to reducing greenhouse gas intensity (emissions per unit of GDP) by 18% (4% more than under existing policies) over 10 years through a combination of voluntary, incentive-based, and existing mandatory measures focused on energy efficiency and other measures. This is projected to attain a 4.5% reduction from forecast emissions in 2012. The Administration has proposed this policy in place of the Kyoto Protocol, which it opposes due to concerns that it could raise energy prices and slow economic growth. Further, the Administration has stated its intent to support funding for energy efficiency and renewable energy programs at DOE and at the Global Environment Facility.

The 2001 *White House Initial Review on Climate Change* cites an existing array of energy efficiency and other programs that support goals of the UNFCCC and refers to the National Energy Policy (NEP) report's provisions for CHP, CAFE, Energy Star, and other energy efficiency policies as part of the foundation for its strategy to curb greenhouse gas (GHG) emissions.

The Kyoto Protocol had called for the United States to cut GHG emissions to 7% below the 1990 level during the period from 2008 to 2012. At the Seventh Conference of Parties (COP-7) in 2001, the United States was accused of avoiding real efforts to reduce emissions, through energy efficiency and other means, in order to address the Kyoto Protocol. At COP-10 in 2004, the parties focused mainly on technical issues, including "next steps" for developing nations. In February 2005, the Kyoto Protocol went into effect, without a U.S. commitment to an emissions reduction goal.

DOE's 2000 report *Scenarios for a Clean Energy Future* shows the potential for advanced energy efficiency and other measures to cut two-thirds of the projected U.S. carbon emissions growth by 2010 and to cut emissions to the 1990 level by 2020. Assuming no major future policy actions, the reference case scenario in the EIA's January 2003 *Annual Energy Outlook 2003* projects 2010 emissions will be 1,800 MMTC, 32% more than that for 1990. DOE's 1995 report *Energy Conservation Trends* shows that energy efficiency has reduced long-term rates of fossil energy use and thereby curbed emissions of CO_2 significantly. (For details about the potential for energy efficiency to reduce CO_2 emissions, see CRS Report RL30414, *Global Climate Change: The Role for Energy Efficiency*.)

In September 2004, the California Air Resources Board approved a plan that would require automobile manufacturers to cut carbon dioxide and other GHG emissions 22% by 2012. This could force automakers to increase fuel efficiency sharply. An industry court challenge is possible. Seven northeastern states have adopted other auto emission regulations by California. In Apil 2005, the Canadian government signed a "voluntary" agreement with automakers to reduce GHG by 5.3 million tons, or 17%, by 2010.

Electric Industry Restructuring and Conservation

The debate over the federal role in restructuring includes questions about energy efficiency. The 2001 electricity problems in California raised the issue of whether a federal role is needed to encourage demand-side energy efficiency and load management measures. A June 2002 report (#49733) by the Lawrence Berkeley National Laboratory, *California Consumers Kept Lights on During Electricity Crisis by Conserving and Investing in Efficient Equipment*, found that conservation and efficiency measures reduced summer 2001 peak demand by 10%, increased system reliability, avoided some wholesale power purchases, and avoided $2 billion to $20 billion in potential losses from rolling blackouts. *Energy Efficiency Leadership in California*, an April 2003 report by the Natural Resources Defense Council and Silicon Valley Manufacturing Group, uses California Energy Commission data to project that additional efficiency measures could reduce electric demand by 5,900 megawatts (MW) and save $12 billion over the next 10 years.

Many states and electric utilities created demand-side management (DSM) programs to promote energy efficiency and other activities as a less costly alternative to new supply. DSM became a significant part of the nation's energy efficiency effort. Utility DSM spending peaked in 1994 at $2.7 billion and DSM energy savings peaked in 1996 at 61 billion kilowatt-hours (which is equivalent to the output from 12 one-gigawatt powerplants).

After California issued its 1994 proposal for electric industry restructuring, many states and utilities reduced DSM efforts. By 1998, utility DSM spending had fallen to about $1.4 billion. In response, some states, such as California, include provisions for energy efficiency and conservation in their restructuring legislation. For example, California's law (A.B. 1890, Article 7) placed a "public goods" charge on all electricity bills from 1998 through 2001 that provided $872 million for "cost effective" energy efficiency and conservation programs. Other states, such as Pennsylvania, have few if any provisions for energy efficiency.

LEGISLATION

109th Congress

H.R. 6 (Barton)

Energy Policy Act of 2005. Section 102 sets a goal for 20% energy reduction in federal facilities by 2015. Section 104 requires federal agency purchases of EPA Energy Star and FEMP-designated products. Section 105 permanently extends ESPCs and sets $500 million cap. Section 124 authorizes funding to states for rebates to support the cost premium for residential purchases of Energy Star products. Section 133 establishes energy efficiency standards for a variety of consumer products and commercial equipment. Title I also sets out several energy efficiency provisions for public housing. Title VII has provisions for hybrid, fuel cell, and electric vehicles; and revises and extends some aspects of fuel economy standards. Title IX reauthorizes DOE energy efficiency R&D programs. Section 1253 would, under certain conditions, terminate PURPA cogeneration requirements. Sections 1312 and 1317 would create $397 million in tax credits for energy efficiency. Committee on Energy and Commerce ordered committee print reported, as amended, April 13. Incorporated Domestic Energy Security Act and H.R. 1541 (as Title XIII). Referred to Committees on Energy and Commerce, Resources, Ways and Means, Science, and others April 18. Passed House, amended, April 21.

H.R. 1541 (Thomas)

Section 202 provides a 15% business investment tax credit to support installation of fuel cell equipment. The Joint Committee on Taxation scores this provision at $6 million over 10 years. Section 207 provides a 20% investment tax credit ($2,000 maximum) to home owners for energy efficiency improvements. The Joint Committee on Taxation scores this provision at $391 million over 10 years. Committee on Ways and Means ordered bill reported, April 13. Incorporated into H.R. 6.

H.R. 2419 (Hobson)

Energy and Water Development Appropriations Act, 2006. Provides funding for DOE energy efficiency (conservation) programs, formerly funded under Interior Appropriations, in a new account structure that merges program funding for DOE renewable energy programs. Reported (H.Rept. 109-86) May 18, 2005. Passed House, amended, May 24.

S. 726 (Alexander)

Natural Gas Price Reduction Act of 2005. Section 101 authorizes funding for an energy conservation public education initiative. Section 102 sets efficiency standards, test procedures, and labeling requirements for several types of residential and commercial equipment. Section 103 authorizes funding for distributed generation. Section 104 authorizes funding to accelerate hydrogen and fuel cell development. Section 105 would, under certain conditions, repeal PURPA Section 210 requirements for cogeneration and small power facilities. Section 106 calls for a study of cogeneration and small power. Introduced April 6, 2005; referred to Committee on Energy and Natural Resources.

S. 727 (Alexander)

Tax Incentives for the Natural Gas Price Reduction Act of 2005. Section 2 makes a 10% investment tax credit available over four years to combined heat and power (CHP or cogeneration) systems smaller than 50 megawatts (MW) that satisfy certain efficiency standards. Section 4 has an investment tax credit (20%) for residential fuel cell equipment. It also creates a 20% investment tax credit ($2,000 maximum) to homeowners for retrofits to existing residential housing with energy efficient envelope components (insulation, windows, roofs, heating equipment); and an equipment tax credit (maximum $2,000) to home builders for envelope components that reduce home energy use by 30%. Section 4 also provides a tax credit to manufacturers ($60 million maximum) for energy-efficient clothes washers ($100 each) and refrigerators ($150 each). Further, Section 4 creates a tax deduction ($1.50 per square foot maximum) for energy efficient equipment in commercial buildings that reduces energy use by 50%. Introduced April 6, 2005; referred to Committee on Finance.

Table 3. DOE Energy Efficiency Budget for FY2004-FY2006
(selected programs, $ millions)

	FY2005 Appn.	FY2006 Request	FY2006 House	FY2006 Senate Cmte	Senate Cmte - House	Senate Cmte - FY2005
HYDROGEN TECH.	94.6	99.1	99.1	99.1	0.0	4.5
FUEL CELL TECH.	74.9	83.6	83.6	83.6	0.0	8.7
Fuel Processor	9.7	9.9	——	——	——	——
Stack Component	32.5	34.0	——	——	——	——
BIOFUELS / BIOREF'Y	89.1	72.2	86.2	92.2	6.0	3.1
VEHICLE TECH.	166.9	165.9	167.9	199.9	32.0	33.0
Hybrid and Electric	——	——	——	——	——	——
Advanced Combustion	——	——	——	——	——	——
Materials Technology	——	——	——	——	——	——
Fuels Technology	——	——	——	——	——	——
Technology Introduction	——	——	——	——	——	——
BUILDING TECH.	67.1	58.0	65.0	67.0	2.0	-0.1
Res. & Commercial Bldgs	21.9	22.9	——	——	——	——
Emerging Technologies	31.4	25.4	——	——	——	——
INDUSTRIAL TECH.	75.3	56.6	56.6	56.5	— 2.4	-18.9
Ind. of the Future, Specific	38.2	22.1	——	——	——	——
Ind. of the Future, Cross.	32.9	30.6	——	——	——	——
DISTRIB. ENERGY RES.*	60.6	56.6	56.6	——	——	——
FED. ENERGY MGMT	20.1	19.2	19.2	19.2	0.0	-0.9
WEATHER'N & INTERG.	309.6	298.2	307.2	325.1	4.0	-1.4
Weatherization Program	224.7	225.4	235.4	240.4	5.0	15.7
State Energy Grants	44.2	41.0	41.0	41.0	0.0	-3.2
State Energy Activities	2.3	0.5	0.5	0.5	0.0	-1.8
Gateway Deployment	35.0	26.7	25.7	26.7	-1.0	-8.3
Rebuild America	——	——	——	6.6	——	——
Clean Cities	——	——	——	6.5	——	——
Energy Star	——	——	——	5.8	——	——
Inventions	——	——	——	2.4	——	——

* Funding for Distributed Energy was moved to the Office of Electricity Delivery and Energy Reliability.

Table 3 Continued

	FY2005 Appn.	FY2006 Request	FY2006 House	FY2006 Senate Cmte	Senate Cmte - House	Senate Cmte - FY2005
PROGRAM MGMT	123.8	117.5	118.0	153.0	0.5	36.5
EFFICIENCY R&D SUBTOTAL	595.8	575.8	——	——	——	——
GRANTS SUBTOTAL	268.9	266.4	276.4	281.4	10.0	12.5
Prior Year Balances	-5.3	——	——	——	——	——
EERE, TOTAL	1,248.9	1,200.4	1,235.8	1,253.8	17.0	4.9

Sources: DOE FY2006 Budget Request, v. 7, Feb. 2005, p 208-214. H.Rept. 109-86 (p. 96-104); S.Rept. 109-84.

108th Congress

P.L. 108-311 (H.R. 1308)

Working Families Tax Relief Act of 2004. Section 318 extends a credit for electric vehicles and Section 319 extends a deduction for clean fuel vehicles. House and Senate approved the conference report (H.Rept. 108-696) September 23, 2004. Signed into law October 4, 2004.

P.L. 108-357 (H.R. 4520)

American Jobs Creation Act. Section 701 creates a $2 billion tax exempt bond program for green building demonstrations at brownfields. Section 910 reduces the tax deduction for Sport Utility Vehicles (SUVs). Introduced in House June 4, 2004. Reported (H.Rept. 108-548, Part 1) June 16. Passed House June 17. In Senate, S. 1637 reported (S.Rept. 108-192) November 3, 2003. S.Amdt. 3562 incorporated S. 1637 into H.R. 4520 and passed Senate July 15, 2004. Conference report (H.Rept. 108-755) approved in House October 7 and in Senate October 11. President signed October 22, 2004.

CONGRESSIONAL HEARINGS, REPORTS AND DOCUMENTS

U.S. Congress. House. Committee on Science. *Improving the Nation's Energy Security: Can Cars and Trucks Be Made More Fuel Efficient?*

Hearing held February 9, 2005. [http://www.house.gov/science/hearings/full05/feb9/February92005.htm]

(A more extensive list appears in CRS Report RL32860, Energy Efficiency and Renewable Energy Legislation in the 109th Congress.)

(Many hearings on Energy Efficiency and Renewable Energy held in the 108th Congress are listed on the DOE Office of Energy Efficiency and Renewable Energy website at [http://www.eere.energy.gov/office_eere/congressional_test.html.])

FOR ADDITIONAL READING

American Council for an Energy-Efficient Economy. Proceedings from the ACEEE 2004 Summer Study on Energy Efficiency in Buildings. Washington, 2004. (10 v.)

——   ACEEE's Green Book: The Environmental Guide to Cars and Trucks: Model Year 2005. 2005. 120 p. Summary at [http://aceee.org/press/0502greencar.htm].

Cato Institute. The High Costs of Federal Energy Efficiency Standards for Residential Appliances. (Policy Analysis No. 504) 2003. 15 p.

Government Accountability Office (GAO). Research and Development: Lessons Learned from Research Could Benefit FreedomCAR Initiative. (GAO -02-8101) 2002. 50 p.

National Association of Regulatory Utility Commissioners (NARUC). *AGA and NRDC*

Release Energy Efficiency (Conservation Tariff) Joint Statement. August 2004. 4 p. [http://www.naruc.org/displayindustryarticle.cfm?articlenbr=21073&startrec=1]

National Research Council. Energy Research at DOE: Was It Worth It? (Energy Efficiency and Fossil Energy Research 1978 to 2000). 2001. 224 p. [http://www.nap.edu/books/0309074487/html/]

——   Effectiveness and Impact of Corporate Average Fuel Economy (CAFE) Standards. 2001. 184 p.

Rocky Mountain Institute. *Winning the Oil Endgame: Innovation for Profits, Jobs, and Security.* 2004. 306 p. [https://www.rmi.org/store/p12details4772.php]

U.S. Department of Energy. Energy Information Administration. *Impacts of Modeled Recommendations of the National Commission on Energy Policy.* [Report on CAFE fuel economy] (SR/OIAF/2005-02) April 2005. 79 p. [http://www.eia.doe.gov/oiaf/servicerpt/bingaman/]

——Interlaboratory Working Group. *Scenarios for a Clean Energy Future.* (ORNL/CON-476) November 2000. 350 p. [http://www.ornl.gov/sci/eere/cef/]

——State Energy Advisory Board. Homeland Security: Safeguarding America's Future with Energy Efficiency and Renewable Energy. (DOE/EE-0272) August 2000. 26 p. [http://www.steab.org/]

U.S. Environmental Protection Agency. *U.S. Climate Action Report 2002.* 2002. 260 p. http://yosemite.epa.gov/oar/globalwarming.nsf/content/ ResourceCenterPublications USClimateActionReport.html].

——   Protecting the Environment — Together: Energy Star and Other Voluntary Programs 2003 Annual Report. (EPA 430-R-04-011) September 2004. 47 p. [http://www.energystar.gov/ia/news/downloads/ annual_report_2003.pdf]

U.S. Government Accountability Office (GAO). Electricity Markets: Consumers Could Benefit from Demand Programs, But Challenges Remain (GAO-04-844) August 2004. 68 p. [http://www.gao.gov/ new.items/d04844.pdf]

WEBSITES

American Council for an Energy-Efficient Economy (ACEEE). Extensive listing of websites on energy efficiency. [http://www.aceee.org/]

National Association of State Energy Offices. [http://www.naseo.org/]

U.S. Council for Automotive Research (USCAR). FreedomCAR. [http://www.uscar.org/freedomcar/index.htm]

U.S. Department of Energy. Energy Efficiency and Renewable Energy Network. [http://www.eere.energy.gov/]

U.S. Department of Energy. FY2005 Congressional Budget Request. [http://www.mbe.doe.gov/budget/05budget/]

U.S. Department of Energy and U.S. Environmental Protection Agency. Fuel Economy. [http://www.fueleconomy.gov/]

U.S. Lawrence Berkeley Laboratory. Center for Building Science. [http://eetd.lbl.gov/]

U.S. Environmental Protection Agency. FY2005 Budget Justification (Goal 1, Clean Air and Global Climate Change, p. I-111 to I-133 and Special Analysis, p. SA-42). [http://www.epa.gov/ocfo/budget/2005/2005cj. htm]

U.S. Environmental Protection Agency. Energy Star Programs. [http://www. energystar.gov/]

In: Energy Efficiency
Editor: Lara S. Zambini, pp. 63-87

ISBN: 1-59454-684-3
© 2006 Nova Science Publishers, Inc.

Chapter 3

ENERGY: USEFUL FACTS AND NUMBERS [*]

Carol Glover and Carl E. Behrens

SUMMARY

Energy supplies and prices are a major economic factor in the United States, and energy markets are volatile and unpredictable. For both these reasons, energy policy is of frequent interest to the Congress. This report presents a statistical view of the supply and consumption of various forms of energy.

After an introductory overview of aggregate energy consumption, the report presents detailed analysis of trends and statistics regarding specific energy sources: oil, electricity, natural gas, and coal. A section on trends in energy efficiency is also presented.

INTRODUCTION

Tracking changes in energy activity is complicated by variations in different energy markets, most of which operate independently. Since aggregate indicators of total energy production and consumption do not adequately reflect these complexities, this compendium focuses on the

---

[*] Excerpted from CRS RL31849 dated April 27, 2005

details of individual activities. Primary among these are oil, particularly gasoline for transportation, and electricity generation and consumption. Natural gas is also an important energy source, particularly in industry and electricity generation. Coal is used almost entirely for electricity generation, nuclear and hydropower completely so.

Solar power and other renewable sources (except hydropower) continue to offer more potential than actual energy production. Conservation and energy efficiency have shown significant gains over the past three decades, however, and offer encouraging potential to relieve some of the dependence on imports that has caused economic difficulties in the past.

To give a general view of energy consumption trends, **Table 1** shows consumption by economic sector — residential, commercial, transportation, and industry — from 1950 to the present. To supplement this overview, some of the trends are highlighted by graphs in **Figures 1 and 2**.

In viewing these figures, a note on units of energy may be helpful. Each source has its own unit of energy. Oil, for instance, is measured in million barrels per day (mbd), coal in million tons per year, natural gas in trillion cubic feet (TCF) per year. To aggregate various types of energy in a single table, a common measure, British Thermal Unit (Btu) is often used. In **Table 1**, energy consumption by sector is given in units of quadrillion Btus per year, or "quads," while per capita consumption is given in million Btus (Mbtu) per year. One quad corresponds to one TCF of natural gas, or approximately 50 million tons of coal. One million barrels per day of oil is approximately 2 quads per year. Approximately 3,600 kilowatt-hours (kwh) of electricity is equivalent to one Mbtu.

From **Table 1** it can be seen that total U.S. energy consumption almost tripled in the half-century from 1950 to 2000, with the industrial sector, the heaviest energy user, growing at the slowest rate. When population increase is accounted for, the growth in energy consumption during the period was about 50%. As **Figure 1** illustrates, much of the growth in per capita energy consumption took place before 1970.

Table 1 does not include consumption of energy by the electricity sector, because it is both a producer and a consumer of energy. For the residential, commercial, industrial and transportation sectors, the consumption figures given are the sum of the resources such as oil and gas that are directly consumed, plus the total energy used to produce the electricity each sector consumed. As **Figure 2** demonstrates, a major trend during the 50-year period was the electrification of the residential and commercial sectors, and also of industry to a lesser extent. By the beginning of the new century, electricity represented 75% of residential energy consumption, 65% of commercial energy consumption, and about a third of industrial energy consumption.

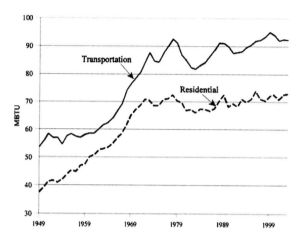

Source: EIA, *Annual Energy Review 2003*, Table 2.1. Population data from the Census Bureau. Per capita data calculated by CRS.

Figure 1. Per Capita Energy Consumption in Transportation and Residential Sectors, 1949-2003

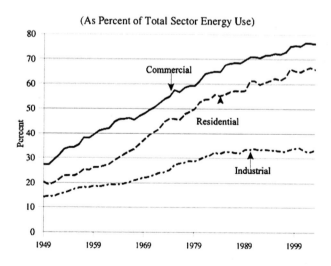

Source: EIA, *Annual Energy Review 2003*, Table 2.1. Percentages calculated by CRS.

Figure 2. Electricity Use: Commercial, Residential, and Industrial Sectors, 1949-2003

Table 1. U.S. Energy Consumption, 1950-2003

	Energy Consumption by Sector (Quads)				Population (million)	Consumption Per Capita (MBtu)		
	Resid.	Comm.	Indus.	Trans.	Total		Resid.	Trans.	Total
1950	6.0	3.9	16.2	8.5	34.6	152.3	39.4	55.8	227.3
1955	7.3	3.9	19.5	9.6	40.2	165.9	44.0	57.6	242.3
1960	9.1	4.6	20.8	10.6	45.1	180.7	50.2	58.7	249.6
1965	10.7	5.8	25.1	12.4	54.0	194.3	55.0	64.0	278.0
1970	13.8	8.3	29.6	16.1	67.8	205.1	67.3	78.5	330.9
1975	14.8	9.5	29.4	18.2	72.0	216.0	68.7	84.5	333.4
1980	15.8	10.6	32.2	19.7	78.3	227.2	69.7	86.7	344.5
1985	16.0	11.5	28.9	20.1	76.5	237.9	67.3	84.4	321.4
1990	17.0	13.3	31.9	22.4	84.7	249.5	68.3	89.9	339.4
1995	18.7	14.7	34.0	23.8	91.2	262.8	71.1	90.7	347.1
2000	20.5	17.2	34.7	26.6	98.9	282.2	72.7	94.1	350.5
2001	20.2	17.3	32.5	26.3	96.4	285.1	71.0	92.2	338.1
2002	20.9	17.6	32.9	26.7	98.0	288.0	72.7	92.6	340.4
2003	21.2	17.5	32.5	26.9	98.2	290.8	73.0	92.4	337.5

Source: Energy Information Administration (EIA), *Annual Energy Review 2003*, Table 2.1.
Population data from the Census Bureau. Per capita data calculated.

Table 2. Energy Consumption in Quads and Percent of Total, 1950-2003

	Petroleum		Natural Gas		Coal		Other		Total
	Quads	%	Quads	%	Quads	%	Quads	%	
1950	13.3	38.4	6.0	17.3	12.3	35.5	3.0	8.7	34.6
1955	17.3	43.0	9.0	22.4	11.2	27.9	2.7	6.7	40.2
1960	19.9	44.1	12.4	27.5	9.8	21.7	3.0	6.7	45.1
1965	23.3	43.1	15.8	29.3	11.6	21.5	3.3	6.1	54.0
1970	29.5	43.4	21.8	32.1	12.3	18.1	4.3	6.3	67.9
1975	32.7	45.4	20.0	27.8	12.7	17.6	6.6	9.2	72.0
1980	34.2	43.7	20.4	26.1	15.4	19.7	8.3	10.6	78.3
1985	30.9	40.4	17.8	23.3	17.5	22.9	10.3	13.5	76.5
1990	33.6	39.7	19.7	23.3	19.2	22.7	12.2	14.4	84.7
1995	34.6	37.9	22.8	25.0	20.1	22.0	13.7	15.0	91.2
2000	38.4	38.8	23.9	24.2	22.6	22.9	13.9	14.1	98.9
2003	39.1	39.8	22.5	22.9	22.7	23.1	13.9	14.2	98.2

Source: EIA, *Annual Energy Review 2003*, Table 1.3. Percentages calculated by CRS.

Consumption of major energy resources — petroleum, natural gas, and coal —is presented in **Table 2**, and shown graphically in **Figure 3**. The historical trends show that petroleum has been and continues to be the major source of energy, rising from about 38% in 1950 to 45% in 1975, then declining to about 40% in response to the energy crisis of the 1970s. Natural gas followed a similar pattern at a lower level, increasing its share of total energy from about 17% in 1950 to over 30% in 1970, then declining to about 20%. Coal, still a major energy source in 1950 at 35%, declined to about 20% a decade later and has remained at about that level since then.

Almost 40% of the energy consumed in the United States is supplied by petroleum, and that proportion has remained approximately the same since 1950, as the data in the previous section show. Also unchanged is the almost total dependence of the transportation sector on petroleum, mostly gasoline.

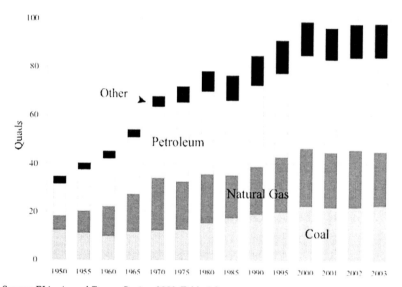

Source: EIA, *Annual Energy Review 2003*, Table 1.3.

Figure 3. Fossil Fuel Consumption, 1950-2003

The perception that the world is on the verge of running out of oil, widespread during the 1970s, has changed, however. The rapid price increases at that time, aided by improved exploration and production technology, stimulated a global search for oil, and resulted in the discovery of large amounts of new reserves. Indeed, as concerns about tightening supply and continually increasing prices were at a peak, proven reserves actually increased by about 50% between 1973 and 1990. Some of the increase was in the Western Hemisphere, mostly in Mexico, but most was located in the region that already dominated the world oil market, the Middle East. With prices essentially steady during the 1990s, the search for oil slowed, but additions to reserves during the decade exceeded the amount of oil pumped out of the ground. By 2003 improved technology for retrieving petroleum from oil sands in Canada, and to a lesser extent heavy oil in Venezuela, led to the addition to proven world reserves of approximately 200 billion barrels, or 20% of the total 1991 figure. These trends are illustrated in **Figure 4**.

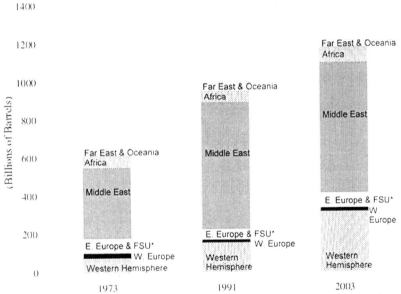

Source: EIA, *International Energy Annual*, 1990 and 2002, Table 8.1 (figures from *Oil and Gas Journal*) * FSU: Former Soviet Union

Figure 4. World Crude Oil Reserves, 1973, 1991, and 2003

Petroleum Consumption, Supply and Imports

Consumption of petroleum by sector reflects a variety of trends. In the residential and commercial sectors petroleum consumption grew steadily from 1950 to 1970, while accounting for about 15% of total petroleum consumption. After the price surge in the 1970s, consumption in those sectors declined, falling to less than 7% of total petroleum consumption. Usage in the electric power sector followed a similar but more abrupt pattern. Until 1970 only about 3% of petroleum went to power generation. In the late 1960s efforts to improve air quality by reducing emissions led utilities to convert a number of coal-fired powerplants to burn oil, and many new plants were designed to burn oil or natural gas. Utilities found themselves committed to increasing dependence on oil just at the time of shortages and high prices; in 1975 almost 9% of oil consumption went for power production. Consumption then fell sharply as alternate sources became available, declining to about 2%-3% of total consumption.

Table 3. Petroleum Consumption by Sector, 1950-2003
(million barrels per day and percent of total)

	Residential-Commercial		Industrial		Electric		Trans-portation		Total
	MBD	%	MBD	%	MBD	%	MBD	%	MBD
1950	1.1	17.2	1.8	28.1	0.2	3.1	3.4	53.1	6.4
1955	1.3	15.3	2.4	28.2	0.2	2.4	4.5	52.9	8.5
1960	1.7	17.3	2.7	27.6	0.2	2.0	5.1	52.0	9.8
1965	1.9	16.5	3.2	27.8	0.3	2.6	6.0	52.2	11.5
1970	2.2	15.0	3.8	25.9	0.9	6.1	7.8	53.1	14.7
1975	1.9	11.7	4.0	24.5	1.4	8.6	9.0	55.2	16.3
1980	1.5	8.8	4.8	28.1	1.2	7.0	9.5	55.6	17.1
1985	1.3	8.3	4.1	26.1	0.5	3.2	9.9	63.1	15.7
1990	1.1	6.5	4.3	25.3	0.6	3.5	11.0	64.7	17.0
1995	1.1	6.2	4.6	26.0	0.3	1.7	11.7	66.1	17.7
2000	1.2	6.1	4.9	24.9	0.5	2.5	13.1	66.5	19.7
2003	1.3	6.5	5.0	25.0	0.5	2.5	13.2	66.0	20.0

Source: EIA, *Annual Energy Review 2003*, Tables 5.13a-d.

Industrial consumption of petroleum, which includes such large consumers as refineries and petrochemical industries, has remained about 25% of total consumption throughout the last half-century. As other sectors' share fell, transportation, which was a little more than half of total consumption prior to 1975, climbed to almost two-thirds by 2000.

Table 4. U.S. Crude Oil Production, 1955-2003
(million barrels per day)

	48 States	Alaska	Total
1955	6.8	—	6.8
1960	7.0	—	7.0
1965	7.8	—	7.8
1970	9.4	0.2	9.6
1975	8.2	0.2	8.4
1980	7.0	1.6	8.6
1985	7.1	1.8	9.0
1990	5.6	1.8	7.4
1995	5.1	1.5	6.6
2000	4.9	1.0	5.8
2003	4.8	1.0	5.7

Source: EIA, *Annual Energy Review 2003*, Table 5.2.

While petroleum consumption increased throughout the last half century (except for a temporary decline following the price surge of the 1970s), U.S. domestic production peaked in 1970 (see **Table 4**). The result, as shown in **Figure 5**, was greater dependence on imported petroleum, which rose from less than 20% in 1960 to more than 50% in 2003.

Petroleum and Transportation

Since the transportation sector is so heavily dependent on petroleum, and uses so much of it, **Table 5** presents a more detailed breakdown of the various types of petroleum used.

Aviation fuel includes both aviation gasoline and kerosene jet fuel. In 1950 aviation was almost entirely gasoline powered; by 2000 it was 99% jet fueled. The growth in flying is illustrated by the fact that aviation fuel was only 3% of petroleum consumption for transportation in 1950, but had grown to 12% in 1965 and has maintained that share since then.

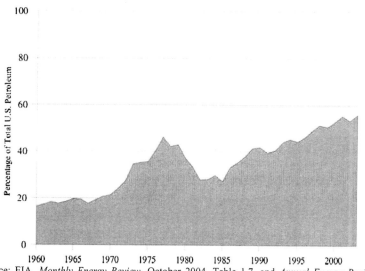

Source: EIA, *Monthly Energy Review*, October 2004, Table 1.7, and *Annual Energy Review 1986*, Table 51.

Figure 5. U.S. Dependence on Imported Petroleum, 1960-2003

Table 5. Transportation Use of Petroleum, 1950-2003 (million barrels per day)

Year	Aviation	Diesel Fuel	Motor Gasoline	Other	Total
1950	0.1	0.2	2.4	0.6	3.4
1955	0.3	0.4	3.2	0.5	4.5
1960	0.5	0.4	3.7	0.4	5.1
1965	0.7	0.5	4.4	0.4	6.0
1970	1.0	0.7	5.6	0.4	7.8
1975	1.0	1.0	6.5	0.4	9.0
1980	1.1	1.3	6.4	0.7	9.5
1985	1.2	1.5	6.7	0.4	9.8
1990	1.5	1.7	7.1	0.5	10.9
1995	1.5	2.0	7.7	0.5	11.7
2000	1.7	2.4	8.4	0.5	13.0
2003	1.6	2.6	8.8	0.2	13.2

Source: EIA, *Annual Energy Review 2003*, Table 5.12c.

Diesel fuel consumption showed a similar dramatic increase. About 6% of total petroleum consumption for transportation in 1950, it rose to 11% by 1975 and to 20% by 2003. Diesel fuel is used by a number of transportation sectors. Part of the increase involved the change of railroads from coal-fired steam to diesel and diesel-electric power. Diesel fuel is used also in the marine transportation sector, and some private automobiles are diesel-powered. The major part of diesel fuel consumption in transportation is by large commercial trucks. Total diesel fuel consumption increased from about 200,000 barrels per day in 1950 to 2.6 million barrels per day in 2003.

Most of the petroleum consumed in the transportation sector is motor gasoline. In 1950 it was 71% of total sector consumption, and by 2003, despite the increase in aviation fuel and diesel, it was 67%. In that half century, gasoline consumption increased by a factor of 3.5. Most motor gasoline is consumed by private vehicles, although commercial small trucks and some large ones are significant users.

Of the other petroleum products consumed in the transportation sector, the largest is residual fuel oil, most of which is used in large marine transport. Consumption of residual fuel oil in the transportation sector was about 500,000 barrels in 1950, and declined gradually to about 400,000 in 2000.

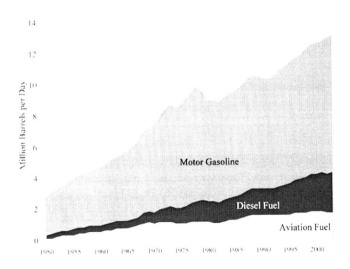

Source: EIA, *Annual Energy Review 2003*, Table 5.12c.

Figure 6. Transportation Use of Petroleum, 1950-2003

Petroleum Prices: Historical Trends

Most commodity prices are typically volatile. Because oil is widely consumed, and is so important at all levels of the economy, its price is closely watched and analyzed. Especially since the 1970s, when a generally stable market dominated by a few large oil companies was broken by the Organization of Petroleum Exporting Countries (OPEC) cartel and a relatively open world market came into being, the price of crude oil has been particularly volatile, as illustrated in **Figure 7**.

At the consumer level, prices of products such as motor gasoline and heating oil have reacted to price and supply disruptions in ways that have been modulated by various government and industry policies and international events. A significant and not often noted fact is that, like many commodities, the long-term trend in gasoline prices, adjusted for inflation and excluding temporary surges, has been down. As shown in **Figure 8**, the real price of gasoline peaked in 1980, then fell precipitously in the mid-1980s. The surge in prices in the summer of 2004 (not shown in the graph) brought the price close to the peak of 1980. (For more current data on gasoline price trends, see CRS Issue Brief IB10134, *Gasoline Prices: Policies and Proposals,* by Carl Behrens.)

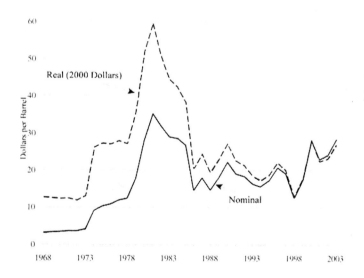

Source: EIA, *Annual Energy Review 2003*, Table 5.21.

Figure 7. Crude Oil Prices, 1968-2003

Source: EIA, *Annual Energy Review 2003*, Table 5.24.

Figure 8. Price per Gallon of Motor Gasoline, 1949-2003

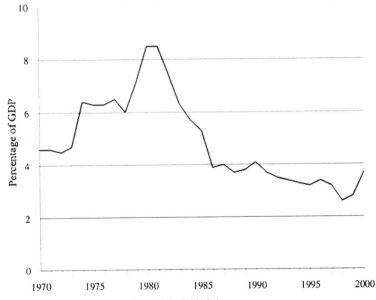

Source: EIA, Annual Energy Review, 2003, Table 3.4.

Figure 9. Consumer Spending on Oil as Percentage of GDP, 1970-2000

Table 6. State Retail Gasoline Taxes

Cents per Gallon Tax

State	Gasoline	Diesel	State	Gasoline	Diesel
Alabama	16¢	19¢	Montana	27¢	27.75¢
Alaska	8¢	8¢	Nebraska	24.8¢	24.8¢
Arizona	18¢	18¢	Nevada	23¢	27¢
Arkansas	21.5¢	22.5¢	New Hampshire	18¢	18¢
California	18¢	18¢	New Jersey	10.5¢	13.5¢
Colorado	22¢	20.5¢	New Mexico	17¢	21¢
Connecticut	25¢	26¢	New York	8¢	8¢
Delaware	23¢	22¢	North Carolina	26.6¢	26.6¢
District of Columbia	22.5¢	22.5¢	North Dakota	21¢	21¢
Florida	14.5¢	27.3¢	Ohio	26¢	26¢
Georgia	7.5¢	7.5¢	Oklahoma	16¢	13¢
Hawaii	16¢	16¢	Oregon	24¢	24¢
Idaho	25¢	25¢	Pennsylvania	30¢	36.4¢
Illinois	19¢	21.5¢	Rhode Island	30¢	30¢
Indiana	18¢	16¢	South Carolina	16¢	16¢
Iowa	20.5¢ [a]	22.5¢	South Dakota	22¢	22¢
Kansas	24¢	26¢	Tennessee	20¢	17¢
Kentucky	16.4¢	12¢	Texas	20¢	20¢
Louisiana	20¢	20¢	Utah	24.5¢	24.5¢
Maine	25.2¢	26.3¢	Vermont	19¢	25¢
Maryland	23.5¢	24.25¢	Virginia	17.5¢	16¢
Massachusetts	21¢	21¢	Washington	28¢	28¢
Michigan	19¢	15¢ [b]	West Virginia	20.5¢	20.5¢
Minnesota	20¢	20¢	Wisconsin	29.1¢	29.1¢
Mississippi	18¢	18¢	Wyoming	14¢	14¢
Missouri	17¢	17¢			

Source: CCH-EXP, STATE-TAX-GUIDE ¶690-100, Motor Fuels Tax Table of Rates. CCH Tax and Accounting. April 2005.

Notes: a. Iowa: Effective 7/1/05, 20.7¢. b. Michigan: 9¢ per gallon when used in commercial vehicles.

The effect of this trend is shown in **Figure 9**, which illustrates the proportion of the gross domestic product (GDP) dedicated to consumer spending on oil. The price surges in the 1970s pushed this ratio from about 4.5% before the Arab oil embargo to about 8.5% following the 1978 crisis in Iran, but since then it has declined to less than 4%.

Gasoline Taxes. Table 6 lists the gasoline and diesel fuel tax rates imposed by each state per gallon of motor fuel, exclusive of local taxes, various environmental taxes and fees, and license and inspection fees. The federal tax on gasoline is currently 18.4 cents per gallon.

Electricity

While overall energy consumption in the United States increased nearly three-fold since 1950, electricity consumption increased even more rapidly. Annual power generation is ten times what it was in 1950. **Figure 10** illustrates the trend.

Throughout this period, coal was used to generate about half the rapidly increasing amount of electricity consumed. Petroleum became briefly important as a source of power generation in the late 1960s because it resulted in lower emissions of air pollutants, but the price surges of the 1970s reversed that trend, and in 2003 only 3% of power generation was oil-fired.

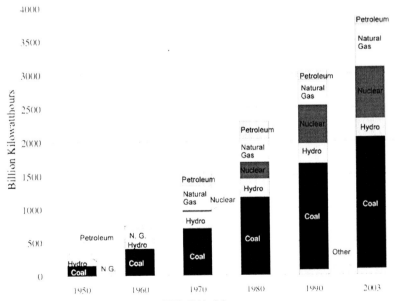

Source: EIA, *Annual Energy Review* 2003, Table 8.2a.

Figure 10. Electricity Generation by Source, Selected Years 1950-2003

Natural gas generation has a more complicated history. Consumption by the electric power industry increased gradually as access by pipeline became more widespread. With the price surge in oil in the 1970s, demand for gas also increased, but interstate prices were regulated, and gas availability declined. In addition, federal energy policy viewed generation of electricity by gas to be a wasteful use of a diminishing resource. The Fuel Use Act of 1978 prohibited new power generators from using gas and set a timetable for shutting down existing gas-fired plants. Gas prices were later deregulated, resulting in increased production, and the Fuel Use Act was repealed, but in the meantime generation of electricity from gas fell from 24% in 1970 to 12% in 1985. In the 1990s gas became more popular, and by 2000 was supplying 16% of total electric generation. Most capacity additions during the late 1990s were gas fired, as illustrated in **Figure 11**. The increased demand contributed to high prices in 2000 that were felt particularly in California.

Nuclear power started coming on line in significant amounts in the late 1960s, and by 1975, in the midst of the oil crisis, was supplying 9% of total generation. However, increases in capital costs, construction delays, and public opposition to nuclear power following the Three Mile Island accident in 1979 curtailed expansion of the technology, and many construction projects were cancelled. Continuation of some construction increased the nuclear share of generation to 20% in 1990, where it remains currently, but no new plants are currently under construction or on order.

Construction of major hydroelectric projects has also essentially ceased, and hydropower's share of electricity generation has gradually declined from 30% in 1950 to 15% in 1975 and less than 10% in 2000. However, hydropower remains highly important on a regional basis.

Sources of power generation vary greatly by region (see **Table 7**). Hydropower in the Pacific Coast states, for instance, supplies 42% of total generation, and natural gas 31%. In 2000, the combination of a drought-caused shortage of hydropower, a tightening of gas supply, and California's new electric regulatory scheme and market manipulation caused very sharp increases in electricity prices in that region. Other regions are heavily dependent on coal generation: the north central and east south central states, as well as the mountain states, generate more than 60% of their electricity from coal, while other regions such as New England and the Pacific Coast use relatively little coal. The west south central region generates 46% of its electricity from gas. New England in the 1970s and 1980s was heavily dependent on oil-generated power; in 2003, despite an increased use of natural gas, oil produced 10% of New England's power, compared to the national average of 3%.

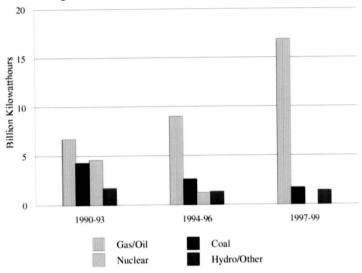

Source: EIA, Inventory of Electric Power Plants, 1990, Inventory of Electric Utility Power Plants, 2000, & Inventory of Nonutility Electric Power Plants, 2000, Table 2.

Figure 11. Capacity Additions, 1990-1999

Table 7. Electricity Generation by Region and Fuel, 2003

Region	Total Generation (billion kwh)	Coal	Petro-leum	Natural Gas	Nuclear	Hydro
New England	127.5	15.4	10.5	34.4	27.3	5.2
Middle Atlantic	399.0	37.3	6.2	11.9	36.3	6.5
East North Central	630.6	71.4	0.5	3.5	22.7	0.5
West North Central	300.4	78.0	0.7	2.3	14.6	3.1
South Atlantic	784.2	53.2	6.5	10.9	24.7	2.4
East South Central	365.8	64.4	1.4	6.4	18.2	7.4
West South Central	572.6	40.3	1.0	43.7	11.2	1.0
Mountain	319.2	67.1	0.2	13.9	9.0	8.9
Pacific Contiguous	330.4	5.1	0.9	30.6	13.1	42.2
Pacific Noncontiguous	18.1	12.1	51.2	22.6	0.0	10.0
U.S. Total	3,848.0	51.2	3.1	16.4	19.8	6.9

Source: EIA, *Electric Power Monthly*, Mar. 2004, Tables 1.6B, 1.7B, 1.8B, 1.9B, 1.11B, and 1.12B.

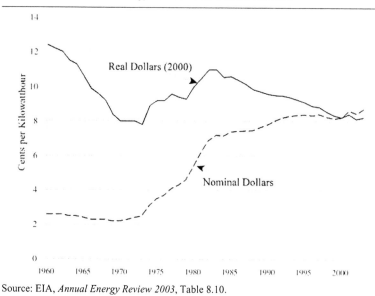

Source: EIA, *Annual Energy Review 2003*, Table 8.10.

Figure 12. Price of Retail Residential Electricity, 1960-2003

OTHER CONVENTIONAL ENERGY RESOURCES

Natural Gas

Consumption of natural gas was about four times as great in 2003 as it was in 1950. Throughout the period, consumption in the residential and commercial sector grew at about the same rate as total consumption, in the range of 30% to 40% of the total. Consumption for electric power generation increased from about 10% in 1950 to more than 20% at the end of the century.

In part because of increased demand by electric utilities, natural gas prices have become extremely volatile in recent years, as illustrated by **Figure 13.**

Table 8. Natural Gas Consumption by Sector, 1950-2002

	Total Consumption (tcf)	Percent Consumed by:		
		Residential-Commercial	Industrial	Electric
1950	5.77	27.5	59.4	10.9
1955	8.69	31.7	52.2	13.3
1960	11.97	34.5	48.2	14.4
1965	15.28	35.0	46.5	15.2
1970	21.14	34.2	43.8	18.6
1975	19.54	38.0	42.8	16.2
1980	19.88	37.0	41.2	18.5
1985	17.28	39.7	39.7	17.6
1990	19.17	36.3	43.1	16.9
1995	22.21	35.1	42.3	19.1
2000	23.33	34.7	39.8	22.3
2001	22.24	34.7	38.1	24.0
2002	23.02	34.4	37.7	24.6
2003	21.89	37.3	37.0	22.5

Source: EIA, *Monthly Energy Review*, October 2004, Table 6.5.

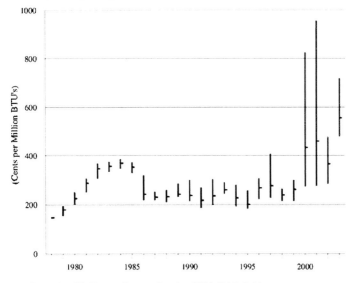

Source: EIA, *Monthly Energy Review*, October 2004, Table 9.11.

Figure 13. Natural Gas Prices to Electric Utilities, 1978-2003

Coal

Consumption of coal about doubled in the half-century from 1950 to 2000, but during that period coal as an energy source changed from a widely used resource to a single-use fuel for generating electricity. In 1950 the residential and commercial sector consumed almost a quarter of total coal consumed; by 1980 less than 1% of coal went to that sector. In transportation, steam locomotives (and some coal-fired marine transportation) consumed 13% of coal; by 1970 they were all replaced with diesel-burning or electric engines. Industry consumed 46% of coal in 1950; by 2000 less than 10% of coal was consumed by that sector. Meanwhile, the electric power sector, which consumed less than 20% of the half-billion tons of coal burned in 1950, used more than 90% of the billion tons consumed in 2003.

Table 9. Coal Consumption by Sector, 1950-2003

	Total Consumption (Million Tons)	Percent Consumed by:			
		Residential-Commercial	Industrial	Transportation	Electric
1950	494.1	23.2	45.5	12.8	18.6
1955	447.0	15.3	48.7	3.8	32.2
1960	398.1	10.3	44.6	0.8	44.4
1965	472.0	5.4	42.6	0.1	51.9
1970	523.2	3.1	35.7	0.1	61.2
1975	562.6	1.7	26.2	—	72.2
1980	702.7	0.9	18.1	—	81.0
1985	818.0	1.0	14.2	—	84.8
1990	904.5	0.7	12.7	—	86.5
1995	962.1	0.6	11.0	—	88.4
2000	1084.1	0.4	8.7	—	90.9
2003	1094.1	0.4	7.8	—	91.8

Source: EIA, *Annual Energy Review 2003*, Table 7.3.

CONSERVATION AND ENERGY EFFICIENCY

Vehicle Fuel Economy

Energy efficiency has been a popular goal of policy makers in responding to the repeated energy crises of recent decades, and efforts to reduce the energy intensity of a broad spectrum of economic activities have been made both at the government and private level. Because of the transportation sector's near total dependence on vulnerable oil supplies, improving the efficiency of motor vehicles has been of particular interest.

Figure 14 illustrates the trends in this effort for passenger cars and for light trucks, vans, and sport utility vehicles, as well as the general lack of improvement in heavy trucks.

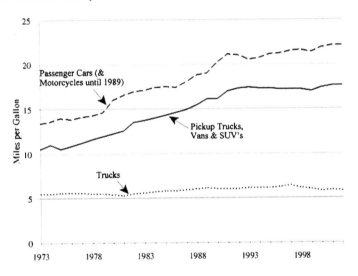

Source: EIA, *Monthly Energy Review*, October 2004, Table 1.9.

Figure 14. Motor Vehicle Rates, 1973-2002

Further analysis by the Environmental Protection Agency (EPA), involving the composition of the fleet as well as the per-vehicle fuel rates, indicates that light vehicle fuel economy has declined on average between 1988 and 2003. This is largely because of increased weight, higher performance, and a higher proportion of sport utility vehicles and light trucks sold. In 2003, SUVs, pickups and vans comprised 48% of all sales, more than twice their market share in 1983

Energy Consumption and GDP

A frequent point of concern in formulating energy policy is the relationship between economic growth and energy use. It seems obvious that greater economic activity would bring with it increased energy consumption, although many other factors affecting consumption make the short-term relationship highly variable. Over a longer period, for some energy-related activities, the relationship with economic growth has been essentially level. For the period from 1973 to 2003, for instance, consumption of electricity remained close to 0.45 kwh per constant dollar of GDP. Similarly, the number of miles driven by all vehicles was close to 3 miles per constant dollar of GDP throughout the same period.

In the case of oil and gas, however, a remarkable drop took place in the ratio of consumption to economic growth following the price spikes and supply disruptions, as illustrated in **Figure 15.** Consumption of oil and gas declined from 14,000 Btus per constant dollar of GDP in 1973 to a little more than 8,000 in 1985, and has continued to decline at a slower rate since then.

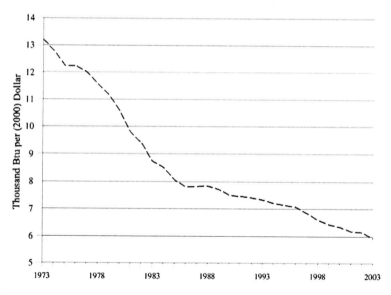

Source: EIA, *Monthly Energy Review*, October 2004, Table 1.8.

Figure 15. Oil and Gas Consumption per Dollar of GDP, 1973-2003

During the earlier period, oil and gas consumption actually declined 15% while GDP, despite many economic problems with inflation and slow growth, was increasing by 44% (see **Figure 16**). During the period 1987 to 2003, oil and gas consumption increased by about 22%, while GDP increased 60%.

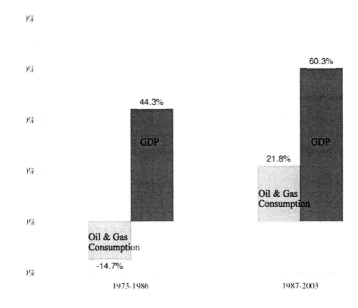

Source: EIA, *Monthly Energy Review*, October 2004, Table 1.8.

Figure 16. Change in Oil and Gas Consumption and Growth in GDP, 1973-2003

MAJOR STATISTICAL RESOURCES

Links to Sources

Most of the tables and figures in this report are derived from data bases maintained by the Department of Energy's Energy Information Administration (EIA). If other or more detailed information is desired, the agency's website presents the complete text of its many statistical reports in PDF format, and also as spreadsheet files in the format of the program Excel. Some of the more important EIA publications are described below. Other sources used in this report are also listed.

Energy Information Administration. [http://www.eia.doe.gov] "The agency's responsibility is to provide timely, high-quality information and to perform objective, credible analyses. ... EIA collects, evaluates, assembles, analyzes, and disseminates data and information relevant to energy resources, reserves, production, demand, technology, and related economic and statistical information."

Annual Energy Review [http://www.eia.doe.gov/aer/contents.html] "The *Annual Energy Review (AER)* presents the Energy Information Administration's historical energy statistics. For many series, statistics are given for every year from 1949 through 2001. The statistics cover all major energy activities, including consumption, production, trade, stocks [inventories], and prices, for all major energy commodities, including fossil fuels, electricity, and renewable energy sources."

Monthly Energy Review [http://www.eia.doe.gov/mer/contents.html] The *Monthly Energy Review* (MER) presents an overview of the EIA's recent monthly energy statistics. The statistics cover the major activities of U.S. production, consumption, trade, stocks (inventories) and prices for petroleum, natural gas, coal electricity, and nuclear energy.

International Energy Annual [http://www.eia.doe.gov/iea/contents.html] The *International Energy Annual* presents information and trends on world energy production and consumption for petroleum, natural gas, coal, and electricity. This report is published to keep the public and other interested parties fully informed of primary energy supplies on a global basis.

Weekly Petroleum Status Report [http://www.eia.doe.gov/oil_gas /petroleum/data_publications/weekly_petroleum_status_report/wpsr.html]. The *Weekly Petroleum Status Report* (WPSR) provides data on supply and selected prices of crude oil and principal petroleum products in the context of historical data and forecasts. Updated every Wednesday morning.

Electric Power Annual [http://www.eia.doe.gov/cneaf/electricity/epa/ epa_sum.html] The *Electric Power Annual* provides a statistical review of the domestic electric power industry for the most recent year including information on; industry capability, generation, fossil-fuel consumption, and stocks. Data on retail sales of electricity and average revenue per kilowatt-hour are also presented.

EIA Quick Stats Pages [http://www.eia.doe.gov/neic/quickstats.html] Coal, Electricity, Natural Gas, Nuclear & Petroleum each have a quick stats page containing a list of 15-20 frequently asked for statistics, often hot-linked to their source documents, and a link to the EIA home page for that subject. This link appears on EIA home page in the top left-hand column.

Other Sources.

Nuclear Regulatory Commission Information Digest [http://www.nrc. gov/reading-rm/doc-collections/nuregs/staff/sr1350/] Updated annually, this official NRC publication (NUREG-1350) includes general statistics on U.S. and worldwide nuclear power production, U.S. nuclear reactors, and radioactive waste.

American Petroleum Institute (API) [http://api-ec.api.org/ newsplashpage/index.cfm] The primary trade association of the oil and natural gas industry representing more than 400 members. Research, programs, and publications on public policy, technical standards, industry statistics, and regulations.

Bloomberg.Com, Market Data: Commodities, Energy Prices [http://www.bloomberg.com/energy/index.html] Displays four tables:

- *Petroleum ($/bbl)* for crude oil. The generally accepted price for crude oil is "WTI Cushing $" which is listed fourth in the table.
- *Petroleum (¢/gal)* for heating oil and gasoline.
- *Natural Gas ($/MMBtu)*
- *Electricity ($/megawatt hour)*

This site is updated two to three times per day.

AAA's Daily Fuel Gauge Report [http://www.fuelgaugereport.com/ index.asp]. At-the-pump retail fuel prices for gasoline and diesel fuel. Gives average price for today, yesterday, a month ago and a year ago for wholesale and crude oil. Also displays line chart showing the averages for the previous 12 months. National, state, and metropolitan data.

International Energy Agency [http://www.iea.org]. The International Energy Agency is an autonomous body within the Organization for Economic Co-operation and Development (OECD). It gathers and analyzes statistics and "disseminates information on the world energy market and seeks to promote stable international trade in energy."

A subscription is required to access most of the information on this Website, although a limited amount of information is available to nonsubscribers. Members of Congress and their staff should contact CRS for a copy of anything that requires a subscription.

Automobile and Light Truck Fuel Economy: The CAFE Standards, by
Robert Bamberger.) . (The EPA study is available online at
[http://www.epa.gov/otaq/fetrends.htm].)

In: Energy Efficiency   ISBN: 1-59454-684-3
Editor: Lara S. Zambini, pp. 89-110   © 2006 Nova Science Publishers, Inc.

Chapter 4

ENERGY TAX POLICY [*]

Salvatore Lazzari

SUMMARY

Historically, U.S. federal energy tax policy promoted the supply of oil and gas. However, the 1970s witnessed (1) a significant cutback in the oil and gas industry's tax preferences, (2) the imposition of new excise taxes on oil, and (3) the introduction of numerous tax preferences for energy conservation, the development of alternative fuels, and the commercialization of the technologies for producing these fuels (renewables such as solar, wind, and biomass, and non-conventional fossil fuels such as shale oil and coalbed methane).

The Reagan Administration, using a free-market approach, advocated repeal of the windfall profit tax on oil and the repeal or phase-out of most energy tax preferences —for oil and gas, as well as alternative fuels. Due to the combined effects of the Economic Recovery Tax Act and the energy tax subsidies that had not been repealed, which together created negative effective tax rates in some cases, the actual energy tax policy differed from the stated policy.

The George H. W. Bush and Bill Clinton years witnessed a return to a much more activist energy tax policy, with an emphasis on energy conservation and alternative fuels. While the original aim was to reduce

---

[*] Excerpted from CRS Report IB10054 dated June 17, 2005

demand for imported oil, energy tax policy was also increasingly viewed as a tool for achieving environmental and fiscal objectives.

The Clinton Administration's energy tax policy emphasized the environmental benefits of reducing greenhouse gases and global climate change, but it will be remembered for its failed proposal to enact a broadly based energy tax based on Btu's (British Thermal Units) and its 1993 across-the-board increase in motor fuels taxes by 4.3¢/gallon. The George W. Bush Administration has proposed a limited number of energy tax measures, but the 106th-108th Congresses have considered comprehensive energy legislation, which included numerous energy tax incentives to increase the supply of, and reduce the demand for, fossil fuels and electricity, and for energy efficiency in residential and commercial buildings as well as for more energy efficient vehicles. They also included tax incentives for several types of alternative and renewable resources such as solar and geothermal. Because of controversy over either corporate average fuel economy standards, the Alaskan national wildlife refuge, or methyl-tertiary butyl ether, each of these attempts failed.

The Working Families Tax Relief Act of 2004 (P.L. 108-311), which was signed into law by the President on October 4, 2004, retroactively extended four energy tax subsidies. The American Jobs Creation Act of 2004 (P.L. 108-357), signed on October 22, 2004, contains several energy-related tax breaks that were in the comprehensive energy bills. The current energy tax structure is dominated by revenues from a long-standing gasoline tax, and tax incentives for alternative and renewable fuels supply relative to energy from conventional fossil fuels.

An $8.1 billion, 11-year energy tax cut was approved by the House as part of comprehensive energy legislation (H.R. 6); the Senate Finance Committee is marking up a $16.1 billion 11-year energy tax package tilted less toward traditional fossil fuels and more toward energy efficiency and renewable fuels than the House bill. The FY2006 budget includes about $6.7 billion in energy tax incentives (over 10 years).

MOST RECENT DEVELOPMENTS

On June 16, 2005, the Senate Finance Committee marked up an $18.4 billion, 11-year energy tax incentives package that includes $14.0 billion in energy tax cuts, and $4.4 billion in tax increases (both energy and non-energy). On April 13, 2005, the House approved a comprehensive energy bill (H.R. 6) with $8.1 billion of energy tax cuts over 11 years. On February 7,

2005, President Bush unveiled his FY2006 budget proposal, which included $6.7 billion in energy tax incentives (over 10 years). On October 4, 2004, the President signed into law the Working Families Tax Relief Act of 2004 (P.L. 108-311), a $146 billion package of tax breaks that retroactively extended four energy tax subsidies. On October 6, 2004, the President signed into law the American Jobs Creation Act of 2004 (P.L. 108-357), containing some of the energy tax breaks that the Congress had been attempting to pass as part of comprehensive energy legislation.

BACKGROUND AND ANALYSIS

Introduction

Energy tax policy involves the use of the government's main fiscal instruments — taxes (financial disincentives) and tax subsidies (or incentives) — to alter the allocation or configuration of energy resources. In theory, energy taxes and subsidies are, like tax policy instruments in general, intended to either correct a problem or distortion in the energy markets or to achieve some social, economic (efficiency, equity, or even macroeconomic), environmental, or fiscal objective. In practice, however, energy tax policy in the United States is made in a political setting, being determined by the views and interests of the key players in this setting: politicians, special interest groups, bureaucrats, and academic scholars. This implies that it does not generally, if ever, adhere to the principles of economic, or public finance, theory alone; that more often than not, energy tax policy may compound existing distortions, rather than correct them.

The idea of applying tax policy instruments to the energy markets is not new, but until the 1970s energy tax policy had been little used, except for the oil and gas industry. Recurrent energy-related problems since the 1970s — oil embargoes, oil price and supply shocks, wide petroleum price variations and price spikes, large geographical price disparities, tight energy supplies, rising oil import dependence, as well as increased concern for the environment — have caused policymakers to look toward energy taxes and subsidies with greater frequency.

This issue brief discusses the history, current posture, and outlook for federal energy tax policy. It also discusses recent energy tax proposals, focusing on the major energy tax provisions that were debated as part of omnibus energy legislation in the 108th Congress (e.g., H.R. 6), which may be reintroduced in the 109th Congress.

Background

The history of federal energy tax policy can basically be divided into four eras: the oil and gas period from 1916 to 1970, the energy crisis period of the 1970s, the free-market era of the Reagan Administration, and the post-Reagan era — including the period since 1998, which has witnessed a plethora of energy tax proposals to address recurring energy market problems.

Energy Tax Policy from 1918 to 1970: Promoting Oil and Gas

Historically, federal energy tax policy was focused on increasing domestic oil and gas reserves and production; there were no tax incentives for energy conservation or for alternative fuels. Two oil/gas tax code preferences embodied this policy: 1) expensing of intangible drilling costs (IDCs) and dry hole costs, which was introduced in 1916, and 2) the percentage depletion allowance, first enacted in 1926 (coal was added in 1932).

Expensing of IDCs (such as labor costs, material costs, supplies, and repairs associated with drilling a well) gave oil and gas producers the benefit of fully deducting from the first year's income ("writing off") a significant portion of the total costs of bringing a well into production, costs that would otherwise (i.e., in theory and under standard, accepted tax accounting methods) be capitalized (i.e., written off during the life of the well as income is earned). For dry holes, which comprised on average about 80% of all the wells drilled, the costs were also allowed to be deducted in the year drilled (expensed) and deducted against other types of income, which led to many tax shelters that benefitted primarily high-income taxpayers. Expensing accelerates tax deductions, defers tax liability, and encourages oil and gas prospecting, drilling, and the development of reserves.

The percentage depletion allowance for oil and gas permitted oil and gas producers to claim 27.5% of revenue as a deduction for the cost of exhaustion or depletion of the deposit, allowing deductions in excess of capital investment (i.e, in excess of adjusted cost depletion) — the economically neutral method of capital recovery for the extractive industries. Percentage depletion encourages faster mineral development than cost depletion (the equivalent of depreciation of plants and equipment).

These and other tax subsidies discussed later (e.g., capital gains treatment of the sale of successful properties, the special exemption from the passive loss limitation rules, and special tax credits) reduced marginal effective tax rates in the oil and gas industries, reduced production costs, and increased investments in locating reserves (increased exploration). They also led to more profitable production and some acceleration of oil and gas production (increased rate of extraction), and more rapid depletion of energy resources than would otherwise occur. Such subsidies tend to channel resources into these activities that otherwise would be used for oil and gas activities abroad or for other economic activities in the United States. Relatively low oil prices encouraged petroleum consumption (as opposed to conservation) and inhibited the development of alternatives to fossil fuels, such as unconventional fuels and renewable forms of energy. Oil and gas production increased from 16% of total U.S. energy production in 1920 to 71.1% of total energy production in 1970 (the peak year).

Energy Tax Policy during the 1970s: Conservation and Alternative Fuels

Three developments during the 1970s caused a dramatic shift in the focus of federal energy tax policy. First, the large revenue losses associated with the oil and gas tax preferences became increasingly hard to justify in the face of increasing federal budget deficits — and in view of the longstanding economic arguments against the special tax treatment for oil and gas. Second, heightened awareness of environmental pollution and concern for environmental degradation, and the increased importance of distributional issues in policy formulation (i.e., equity and fairness), lost the domestic oil and gas industry much political support. Thus, it became more difficult to justify percentage depletion and other subsidies, largely claimed by wealthy individuals and big vertically integrated oil companies. More importantly, during the 1970s there were two energy crises: the oil embargo of 1973 — also known as the first oil shock — and the Iranian Revolution in 1979, which focused policymakers' attention on the problems (alleged "failures") in the energy markets and how these problems reverberated throughout the economy causing stagflation, shortages, productivity problems, rising import dependence, and other economic and social problems.

These developments caused federal energy tax policy to shift from oil and gas supply toward energy conservation (reduced energy demand) and alternative energy sources.

Three broad actions through the tax code were taken to implement the new energy tax policy during the 1970s: First, the oil industry's two major tax preferences — expensing of IDCs and percentage depletion — were significantly reduced, particularly the percentage depletion allowance, which was eliminated for the major integrated oil companies and reduced for the remaining producers. Other oil and gas tax benefits were also cut back during this period. For example, oil- and gas-fired boilers used in steam generation (for example, to generate electricity) could no longer qualify for accelerated depreciation as a result of the Energy Tax Act of 1978 (as discussed below).

The second broad policy action was the imposition of several new excise taxes penalizing the use of conventional fossil fuels, particularly oil and gas (and later coal). The Energy Tax Act of 1978 (ETA, P.L. 95-618) created a federal "gas guzzler" excise tax on the sale of automobiles with relatively low fuel economy ratings. This tax, which is still in effect, currently ranges from $1,000 for an automobile rated between 21.5 and 22.5 miles per gallon (mpg) to $7,700 for an automobile rated at less than 12.5 mpg. Chief among the taxes on oil was the windfall profit tax (WPT) enacted in 1980 (P.L. 96-223). The WPT imposed an excise tax of 15% to 70% on the difference between the market price of oil and a predetermined (adjusted) base price. This tax, which was repealed in 1988, was part of a political compromise that decontrolled oil prices (between 1971 and 1980 oil prices were controlled under President Nixon's Economic Stabilization Act of 1970 — the so-called "wage-price freeze").

Another, but relatively small, excise tax on petroleum was instituted in 1980: the environmental excise tax on crude oil received at a U.S. refinery. This tax, part of the Comprehensive Environmental Response, Compensation, and Liability Act of 1980 (P.L. 96-510), otherwise known as the "Superfund" program, was designed to charge oil refineries for the cost of releasing any hazardous materials that resulted from the refining of crude oil. The tax rate was set initially at 0.79¢ ($0.0079) per barrel, and was subsequently raised to 9.7¢ per barrel. This tax expired at the end of 1995, but legislation has been proposed since then to reinstate it as part of Superfund reauthorization.

The third broad action taken during the 1970s to implement the new and refocused energy tax policy was the introduction of numerous tax incentives or subsidies — special tax credits, deductions, exclusions, etc. — for energy conservation, the development of alternative fuels (renewable and non-conventional fuels), and the commercialization of energy efficiency and alternative fuels technologies. Most of these new tax subsidies were introduced as part of the Energy Tax Act of 1978 and expanded under the WPT, which also introduced additional new energy tax subsidies. The following list describes these:

- *Residential and Business Energy Tax Credits.* The ETA provided income tax credits for homeowners and businesses that invested in a variety of energy conservation products (e.g., insulation and other energy-conserving components) and for solar and wind energy equipment installed in a principal home or a business. The business energy tax credits were 10% to 15% of the investment in conservation or alternative fuels technologies, such as synthetic fuels, solar, wind, geothermal, and biomass. These tax credits were also expanded as part of the WPT but they generally expired (except for business use of solar and geothermal technologies) as scheduled either in 1982 or 1985. President Clinton's FY2001 budget included a solar credit that is very similar to the 1978 residential energy tax credits. A 15% investment tax credit for business use of solar and geothermal energy, which was made permanent, is all that remains of these tax credits.

- *Tax Subsidies for Alcohol Fuels.* The ETA also introduced the excise tax exemption for gasohol, recently at 5.2¢ per gallon out of a gasoline tax of 18.4¢/gal. Subsequent legislation extended the exemption and converted it into an immediate tax credit (currently at 51¢/gallon of *ethanol*).

- *Percentage Depletion for Geothermal.* The ETA made geothermal deposits eligible for the percentage depletion allowance, at the rate of 22%. Currently the rate is 15%.

- *§29 Tax Credit for Unconventional Fuels.* The 1980 WPT included a $3.00 (in 1979 dollars) production tax credit to stimulate the supply of selected unconventional fuels: oil from shale or tar sands, gas produced from either geo-pressurized brine, Devonian shale, tight formations, and coalbed methane, gas from biomass, and synthetic fuels from coal. In current dollars this credit, which is still in effect, was $6.40 per barrel of liquid fuels and about $1.13 per thousand cubic feet (mcf) of gas in 2003.

- *Tax-Exempt Interest on Industrial Development Bonds.* The WPT made facilities for producing fuels from solid waste exempt from federal taxation of interest on industrial development bonds (IDBs). This exemption was for the benefit of the development of alcohol fuels produced from biomass, for solid-waste-to-energy facilities, for hydroelectric facilities, and for facilities for producing renewable energy. IDBs, which provide significant benefits to state and local electric utilities (public power), had become a popular source of financing for renewable energy projects.

Some of these incentives — for example, the residential energy tax credits — have since expired, but others remain and still new ones have been introduced, such as the §45 renewable electricity tax credit, which was introduced in 1992 and expanded under the American Jobs Creation Act of 2004 (P.L. 108-357). The important point is that this approach toward energy tax policy — subsidizing a plethora of different forms of energy (both conventional and renewable) and providing incentives for diverse energy conservation (efficiency) technologies in as many sectors as possible has been the paradigm followed by policymakers since the 1970s. (A significant increase in nontax interventions in the energy markets — laws and regulations, such as the Corporate Average Fuel Economy (CAFÉ) standards to reduce transportation fuel use, and other interventions through the budget and the credit markets — has also been a significant feature of energy policy since the 1970s. This included some of the most extensive energy legislation ever enacted. These non-tax policy measures are not discussed here.)

Reagan's Free-Market Energy Tax Policy

The Reagan Administration opposed using the tax law to promote either oil and gas development, energy conservation, or the supply of alternative fuels. The idea was to have a more neutral and less distortionary energy tax policy, which would make energy markets work more efficiently and generate benefits to the general economy. The Reagan Administration believed that the responsibility for commercializing conservation and alternative energy technologies rested with the private sector and that high oil prices — real oil prices (corrected for inflation) were at historically high levels in 1981 and 1982 — would be ample encouragement for the development of alternative energy resources. High oil prices in themselves create conservation incentives and stimulate oil and gas production.

President Reagan's free-market views were well known prior to his election. During the 1980 presidential campaign, he proposed repeal of the WPT, deregulating oil and natural gas prices, and minimizing government intervention in the energy markets. The Reagan Administration's energy tax policy was professed more formally in several energy and tax policy studies, including its 1981 National Energy Policy Plan and the 1983 update to this plan; it culminated in a 1984 Treasury study on general tax reform, which also proposed fundamental reforms of federal energy tax policy. In terms of actual legislation, many of the Reagan Administration's objectives were realized, although as discussed below there were unintended effects. In 1982, the business energy tax credits on most types of non-renewable technologies — those enacted under the ETA of 1978 — were allowed to expire as scheduled; other business credits and the residential energy tax credits were allowed to expire at the end of 1985, also as scheduled. Only the tax credits for business solar, geothermal, ocean thermal and biomass technologies were extended. And as mentioned above, today the tax credit for business investment in solar and geothermal technologies, which has since been reduced to 10%, is all that remains of these tax credits. A final accomplishment was the repeal of the WPT, but not until 1988, the end of the Reagan term. The Reagan Administration's other energy tax policy proposals, however, were not adopted. The tax incentives for oil and gas were not eliminated, although they were pared back as part of the Tax Reform Act (TRA) of 1986.

While the Reagan Administration's objective was to create a free-market energy policy, significant liberalization of the depreciation system and reduction in marginal tax rates —both the result of the Economic Recovery Tax Act of 1981 (ERTA, P.L. 97-34) — combined with the regular investment tax credit and the business energy investment tax credits, resulted in negative effective tax rates for many investments, including alternative energy investments such as solar and synthetic fuels. Also, the retention of percentage depletion and expensing of IDCs (even at the reduced rates) rendered oil and gas investments still favored relative to investments in general.

Energy Tax Policy after Reagan

After the Reagan Revolution, several major energy and non-energy laws were enacted that amended the energy tax laws in several ways, some major:

- *Revenue Provisions of the Omnibus Reconciliation Act of 1990.* President George H. W. Bush's first major tax law included numerous energy tax incentives: (1) For conservation (and deficit reduction), the law increased the gasoline tax by 5¢/gallon and doubled the gas-guzzler tax; (2) for oil and gas, the law introduced a 10% tax credit for enhanced oil recovery expenditures, liberalized some of the restrictions on the percentage depletion allowance, and reduced the impact of the alternative minimum tax on oil and gas investments; and (3) for alternative fuels, the law expanded the §29 tax credit for unconventional fuels and introduced the tax credit for small producers of ethanol used as a motor fuel.
- *Energy Policy Act of 1992 (P.L. 102-486).* This broad energy measure introduced the §45 tax credit, at 1.5¢ per kilowatt hour, for electricity generated from wind and "closed-loop" biomass systems.

(Poultry litter was added later. For new facilities, this tax credit expired at the end of 2001 and again in 2003 but has been retroactively extended by recent tax legislation (as discussed below.) In addition, the 1992 law 1) added an income tax deduction for the costs, up to $2,000, of clean-fuel powered vehicles; 2) liberalized the alcohol fuels tax exemption; 3) expanded the §29 production tax credit for non-conventional energy resources; 4) liberalized the tax breaks for oil and gas.

- *Omnibus Budget Reconciliation Act of 1993 (P.L. 103-66)*. President Clinton proposed a differential Btu tax on fossil fuels (a broadly-based general tax primarily on oil, gas, and coal based on the British thermal units of heat output), which was dropped in favor of a broadly applied 4.3¢/gallon increase in the excise taxes on motor fuels, with revenues allocated for deficit reduction rather than the various trust funds.
- *Taxpayer Relief Act of 1997 (P.L. 105-34)*. This law includes a variety of excise tax provisions for motor fuels, of which some involved tax reductions on alternative transportation fuels, and some involved increases, such as on kerosene, which on balance further tilted energy tax policy toward alternative fuels.
- *Tax Relief and Extension Act*. Enacted as Title V of the Ticket to Work and Work Incentives Improvement Act of 1999 (P.L. 106-170), it extended and liberalized the 1.5¢/kWh renewable electricity production tax credit, and renewed the suspension of the net income limit on the percentage depletion allowance for marginal oil and gas wells.

As this list suggests, the post-Reagan energy tax policy returned more to the interventionist course established during the 1970s and primarily was directed at energy conservation and alternative fuels, mostly for the purpose of reducing oil import dependence and enhancing energy security. However, there is an environmental twist to energy tax policy during this period, particularly in the Clinton years. Fiscal concerns, which for most of that period created a perennial search for more revenues to reduce budget deficits, have also driven energy tax policy proposals during the post-Reagan era. This is underscored by proposals, which have not been enacted, to impose broad-based energy taxes such as the Btu tax or the carbon tax to mitigate greenhouse gas emissions.

Another interesting feature of the post-Reagan energy tax policy is that while the primary focus continues to be energy conservation and alternative fuels, no energy tax legislation has been enacted during this period that does not also include some, relatively minor, tax relief for the oil and gas industry, either in the form of new tax incentives or liberalization of existing tax breaks (or both).

Energy Tax Incentives in Comprehensive Energy Legislation

Several negative energy market developments since about 1998, which some had characterized as an "energy crisis," had led to congressional action on comprehensive energy proposals, which included numerous energy tax incentives. And with the exception of two recent tax bills enacted in October 2004, which included a limited number of sundry energy tax incentives, each of these bills has failed.

Brief History of Comprehensive Energy Policy Proposals

Although the primary rationale for comprehensive energy legislation has been spiking petroleum prices, and to a lesser extent spiking natural gas and electricity prices, the origin of these bills was the very low crude oil prices of the late 1990s. Domestic crude oil prices reached a low of just over $10 per barrel in the winter of 1998-1999, among the lowest crude oil prices in history after correcting for inflation. From 1986-1999 oil prices averaged about $17 per barrel, fluctuating from between $12 and $20 per barrel. These low oil prices hurt oil producers, benefitted oil refiners, and encouraged consumption. They also served as a disincentive to conservation and investment in energy efficiency technologies and discouraged production of alternative fuels and renewable technologies. To address the low oil prices, there were many tax bills in the first session of the 106th Congress (1999) focused on production tax credits for marginal or stripper wells, but they also included carryback provisions for net operating losses, and other fossil fuels supply provisions.

By summer 1999, crude oil prices rose to about $20 per barrel, and peaked at more than $30 per barrel by summer 2000, causing high gasoline, diesel, and heating oil prices. To address these effects of high crude oil prices, legislative proposals again focused on production tax credits and other supply incentives. The rationale was not tax relief for a depressed industry but tax incentives to increase output, reduce prices, and provide price relief to consumers.

In addition to high petroleum prices there were forces — some of which were understood (factors such as environmental regulations and pipeline breaks) and others that are still are not so clearly understood — that caused the prices of these petroleum products to spike. In response, there were proposals in 2000 to either temporarily reduce or eliminate the federal excise tax on gasoline, diesel, and other special motor fuels. The proposals aimed to help consumers (including truckers) cushion the financial effect of the price spikes. (For an analysis of this legislation, see CRS Report RL30497, *Suspending the Gas Tax: Analysis of S. 2285.*) The Midwest gasoline price spike in summer 2000 kept interest in these excise tax moratoria alive and generated interest in proposals for a windfall profit tax on oil companies which, by then, were earning substantial profits from high prices.

Despite numerous bills to address these issues, no major energy tax bill was enacted in the 106th Congress. However, some minor amendments to energy tax provisions were enacted as part of non-energy tax bills. This includes Title V of the Ticket to Work and Work Incentives Improvement Act of 1999 (P.L. 106-170), enacted on December 1999. Also, the 106th Congress did enact a package of $500 million in loan guarantees for small independent oil and gas producers, which became law (P.L. 106-51) in August 1999.

Energy Tax Action in the 107th Congress

In early 2001, the 107th Congress faced a combination of fluctuating oil prices, an electricity crisis in California, and spiking natural gas prices. The gas prices had increased steadily in 2000 and reached $9 per thousand cubic feet (mcf) at the outset of the 107th Congress. At one point, spot market prices reached about $30 per mcf, the energy equivalent of $175 per barrel of oil. The combination of energy problems had developed into an "energy crisis," which prompted congressional action on a comprehensive energy policy bill — the first since 1992 — which included a significant expansion of energy tax incentives and subsidies and other energy policy measures.

In 2002, the House and Senate approved two distinct versions of an omnibus energy bill, H.R. 4. While there were substantial differences in the non-tax provisions of the bill, the energy tax measures also differed significantly. The House bill proposed larger energy tax cuts, with some energy tax increases. It would have reduced energy taxes by about $36.5 billion over 10 years, in contrast to the Senate bill, which cut about $18.3 billion over 10 years, including about $5.1 billion in tax credits over 10 years for two mandates: a renewable energy portfolio standard ($0.3 billion) and a renewable fuel standard ($4.8 billion). The House version emphasized conventional fuels supply, including capital investment incentives to stimulate production and distribution of oil, natural gas, and electricity. This focus assumed that recent energy problems were due mainly to supply and capacity shortages driven by economic growth and low energy prices. In comparison, the Senate bill would have provided a much smaller amount of tax incentives for fossil fuels and nuclear power and somewhat fewer incentives for energy efficiency, but provided more incentives for alternative and renewable fuels. The conference committee on H.R. 4 could not resolve differences, so the bills were dropped on November 13, 2002.

Energy Tax Action in the 108th Congress

On the House side, on April 3, 2003, the Ways and Means Committee (WMC) voted 24-12 for an energy tax incentives bill (H.R. 1531) that was incorporated into H.R. 6 and approved by the House on April 11, 2003, by a vote of 247-175. The House version of H.R. 6 provided about $17.1 billion of energy tax incentives and included just under $0.1 billion ($83 million) of non-energy tax increases, or offsets. This bill was a substantially scaled-down version of the House energy tax bill H.R. 2511 (107th Congress), which was incorporated into H.R. 4, the House energy bill of the 107th Congress that never became law. After returning from the August 2003 recess, a House and Senate conference committee negotiated differences among provisions in three energy policy bills: the House and Senate versions of H.R. 6, and a substitute to the Senate Finance Committee (SFC) bill — a modified (or amended) version of S. 1149 substituted for Senate H.R. 6 in conference as S.Amdt. 1424 and S.Amdt. 1431.

On November 14, 2003, House and Senate conferees reconciled the few remaining differences over the two conference versions of H.R. 6, which primarily centered on several energy tax issues — ethanol tax subsidies, the §29 unconventional fuels tax credit, tax incentives for nuclear power, and clean coal. On November 18, 2003, the House approved, by a fairly wide margin (246-180), the conference report containing about $23.5 billion of energy tax incentives. However, with the proposed ethanol mandate, which would further reduce energy tax receipts — the 10-year revenue loss was projected to be around $26 billion. On November 24, Senate Republicans put aside attempts to enact H.R. 6. A number of uneasy alliances pieced together to bridge contentious divides over regional issues as varied as electricity, fuel additives (MTBE), and natural gas subsidies, failed to secure the necessary 60 votes to overcome a Democratic filibuster before Congress's adjournment for the holiday season. This represented the third attempt to pass comprehensive energy legislation, a top priority for Republicans and for President Bush.

Republicans introduced a smaller energy bill as S. 2095 on February 12, 2004. S. 2095 included a slightly modified version of the amended energy tax bill S. 1149; the tax provisions of S. 2095 were added to the export tax repeal bill S. 1637, on April 5, 2004. The Senate approved S. 1637, with the energy tax measures, on May 11. H.R. 4520, the House version of the export tax repeal legislation, did not contain energy tax measures; they were still incorporated into H.R. 6.

Energy Tax Provisions in the Working Families Tax Relief Act of 2004.

After some existing energy tax incentives expired, the 108th Congress enacted retroactive extension of several of the provisions as part of the Working Families Tax Relief Act of 2004 (P.L. 108-311), a $146 billion package of middle class and business tax breaks. This legislation, which was signed into law by the President on October 4, 2004, retroactively extended four energy tax subsidies: the §45 renewable tax credit, suspension of the 100% net income limitation for the oil and gas percentage depletion allowance, the $4,000 tax credit for electric vehicles, and the deduction for clean fuel vehicles (which ranges from $2,000 to $50,000). The §45 tax credit and the suspension of the 100% net income limitation had each expired on January 1, 2004; they were retroactively extended through December 31, 2005.

The electric vehicle credit and the clean-vehicle income tax deduction were being phased out gradually beginning on January 1, 2004. P.L. 108-311 arrests the phase-down — provides 100% of the tax breaks — through 2005, but resumes it beginning on January 1, 2006, when only 25% of the tax break will be available. (For more information, see CRS Report RL32265, *Expired and Expiring Energy Tax Incentives*.)

Energy Tax Provisions of the "Jobs" Bill. After the Congress repeatedly chose not to enact a more extensive list of energy tax incentives for energy efficiency, renewable fuels, and for oil, gas, and coal, it agreed to a scaled down package of energy tax incentives from the Senate-passed version of the FSC-ETI "jobs" bill (H.R. 4520). This bill, enacted as the American Jobs Creation Act of 2004 (P.L. 108-357) on October 22, 2004, contains several energy-related tax breaks:

- Expansion of the renewable electricity credit to open-loop biomass, geothermal, solar, small irrigation power, and municipal solid waste facilities, and creating the production tax credit for refined coal. The latter provides a new tax credit of $4.375/ton for refined coal — not for the electricity produced from the coal. (The refined coal tax credit was originally part of the proposed expansion of the §29 tax credit, which already benefits "synfuels" from coal and was inserted into the renewable electricity section of the tax code). Expansion of the §45 tax credit also includes minimum tax relief.

- Liberalization of the tax treatment of electric cooperatives under a restructured electricity market.
- Treatment of certain Alaska pipeline property as seven-year depreciation property (rather than 15 years under prior law) and extension of the 15% enhanced oil recovery credit to Alaska gas processing facilities.
- Reform of the tax subsidies for fuel ethanol — basically replacement of the excise tax exemption with an equivalent immediate tax credit — and expansion of the credit to include biodiesel (at a higher rate for biodiesel made from virgin oils). Liberalization includes allowance of the credits against the alternative minimum tax.
- Creation of a new tax credit for oil and gas from marginal (small) wells; this credit is triggered when oil prices are below $18/barrel ($2/mcf for natural gas), which means that currently, with oil prices above $40/barrel, it would provide no benefits.
- Repeal of the general fund component (4.3¢/gal.) excise tax on diesel fuel used in trains and barges.
- A $2.10/barrel tax credit for production of low-sulfur diesel fuel and "expensing" of (basically, faster depreciation deductions for) the capital costs to produce such fuels. Both tax subsidies are subject to limits.
- A host of provisions to prevent fuel tax fraud, including one changing the collection point of the tax on aviation fuels.

Current Posture of Energy Tax Policy

The above background discussion of energy tax policy may be conveniently summarized in **Table 1,** which shows current energy tax provisions — both taxes and tax subsidies —and related revenue effects. A minus ("- ") sign indicates revenue losses, which means that the provision is a tax subsidy or incentive, intended to increase the subsidized activity (energy conservation measures or the supply of some alternative and renewable fuel or technology); no minus sign means that the provision is a tax, which means that it should reduce supply of, or demand for, the taxed activity (either conventional fuel supply, energy demand, or the demand for energy-using technologies, such as cars).

Energy Tax Policy Outlook

Expanded tax subsidies (incentives) for energy supply and conservation have been an integral, if not the dominant, part of comprehensive energy policy proposals over the last five years. Congress has tried unsuccessfully for the past four years to pass a comprehensive energy bill — three of the last four bills have stalled in the Senate — one of the top legislative priorities of Republicans and the Bush Administration.

Some energy tax incentives were enacted as part of the Working Families Tax Relief Act of 2004 (P.L. 108-311), enacted on October 4, 2004; about $5 billion in energy tax incentives were part of the American Jobs Creation Act of 2004 (P.L. 108-357) enacted on October 22, 2004. About $8.1 billion in energy tax cuts have been incorporated in H.R. 6, (109th Congress), which was approved by the House on April 21, 2005, by a vote of 249 to 183. However, that leaves roughly $10.4 billion in tax breaks embodied in the failed comprehensive legislation H.R. 6 (108th Congress) that have been dropped.

H.R. 6 (The Energy Policy Act of 2005)

The energy tax cuts of H.R. 6 (109th Congress) were approved by the House Ways and Means Committee as H.R. 1541, Enhanced Energy Infrastructure and Technology Act of 2005, on April 13, 2005. This bill proposes an $8.1 billion, 11-year tax cut of energy taxes, weighed almost entirely toward fossil fuels and electricity. The Senate Finance Committee has marked up the Energy Policy Tax Incentives Act of 2005, an $18.4 billion, 11-year energy tax cut tilted less toward fossil fuel production and more toward energy conservation and alternative fuels than the House measure. The SFC bill includes $4.4 billion of tax increases (mostly non-energy but also some energy tax increases) and $0.2 billion of non-energy tax cuts. The distribution of the cuts by type of fuel for each of the two bills is shown in **Table 2.**

Table 1. Current Energy Tax Incentives and Taxes: Estimated Revenue Effects FY2005 and FY2005-FY2009 ($ millions)

Category	Provision	Major Limitations	Revenue Effects FY2005	Revenue Effects FY2005-FY2009
CONVENTIONAL FOSSIL FUELS SUPPLY (bpd = barrels per day; < indicates less than)				
% depletion — oil, -gas, and coal	15% of sales (higher for marginal wells); 10% for coal	for indep., up to 1,000 or equiv. bpd	-$500	-2,700
expensing of IDC's — oil/gas & other fuels	100% deductible in first year	corporations expense only 70% of IDC's	- 500	-2,300
enhanced oil recovery credit	15% of the costs	only for specific tertiary methods	- 300	-2,000
incentives for small refiners to comply with EPA sulfur regulations	$2.10 credit per barrel of low-sulfur diesel, + expensing of 75% of capital costs	credit limited to 25% of capital costs; expensing phases out for refining capacity of 155,000-205,000 barrels per day.	< - 50	< - 50
black-lung coal excise taxes and AML fees(2003)	$1.25/ton for underground coal ($0.90 for surface coal)	coal tax not to exceed 4.4% of sales price (2.2% for the AML fee)	789	NA
disposition of elec. trans. property to implement FERC policy	capital gain recognized evenly over 8 years	proceeds must be reinvested in other elec. assets	- 2,700	-2,600
ALTERNATIVE, UNCONVENTIONAL, AND RENEWABLE FUELS				
§29, production tax credit	$6.40/bar. of oil or($1.13/mcf of gas)	biogas, coal synfuels, coalbed methane, etc.	- 1,200	- 4,900
credits for fuel ethanol	$0.51 blender's credit, + $0.10/gal small producer credit	for biomass ethanol only (e.g., from corn)	- 1,490	- 7,900
tax credits for biodiesel	$0.50/gal. of recycled biodiesel; $1.00/gal. for virgin biodiesel	sold at retail or used in a trade or business; applies to oils from vegetables or animal fats	< - 50	< - 50

Table 1.Continued

Category	Provision	Major Limitations	Revenue Effects FY2005	Revenue Effects FY2005-FY2009
§45 credit for renewable electricity	1.8¢/kWh. (0.9¢ in some cases; $4.375/ton of refined coal	wind, closed-loop biomass, poultry waste, solar, geothermal, et. al.	- 300	- 2,000
exclusion of interest on S&L bonds	interest income exempt from tax	for hydroelectric or biomass facilities used to produce electricity	-200	- 1,000
deduction for clean-fuel and hybrid vehicles	$2,000 for cars; $50,000 for trucks; $100,000 deduction for refueling facilities	CNG, LNG, LPG, hydrogen, neat alcohols, and electricity; phases out over 2006	- 120	- 70
tax credit for electric vehicles	10%, up to $4,000	phase-out in 2006	< - 50	< - 50
credit for solar & geothermal tech.	10% investment tax credit for businesses	utilities excluded	< - 50	< - 50
ENERGY CONSERVATION				
fuels taxes (FY2003)*	18.4¢/gal of gas	4.4¢-24.4¢ for other fuels	39,078	204,869
mass trans. subsidies	exclusion of $105/month	up to $190/month for parking benefits	- 4,000	- 21,400
gas-guzzler tax (FY2003)	$1,000-$7,700/ vehicle weighing 6,000 lbs. or less	trucks and SUV's are exempt	127	NA
exclusion for utility conservation subsidies	subsidies not taxable as income	any energy conservation measure	< - 50	< - 50

Source: Joint Tax Committee estimates and Internal Revenue Service data.

Note: A negative sign indicates a tax subsidy or incentive; no negative sign indicates an energy tax. NA denotes not available. * This category includes revenue from excise taxes on tires, a heavy vehicle use tax, and retail sales tax on trucks and tractors, which also go into the Highway Trust Fund (HTF). No separate breakdown of revenue losses for fuels is available for FY2005-FY2009, but revenues from motor fuel taxes generally represent about 90% of the total HTF taxes.

Table 2. Energy Tax Provisions in the House and SFC Bill (109th Congress): Comparison of 11-Year Estimated Revenue Loss by Type of Incentive ($ millions; % of total revenue losses)

	House H.R. 6		SFC Bill a	
INCENTIVES FOR FOSSIL FUELS SUPPLY				
(1)	(2)	(3)	(4)
(1) Oil & Gas Production	-$1,525	18.9%	-$1,416	7.8%
(2) Oil & Gas Refining and Distribution	-1,663	20.6%	-1,408	7.7%
(3) Coal	-1,490	18.4%	-2,996	15.5%
(4) Subtotal	-4,678	57.8%	-5,820	29.9%
ELECTRICITY RESTRUCTURING PROVISIONS				
(5) Nuclear	-1,313	16.2%	-278	1.5%
(6) Other	-1,529	18.9%	-475	2.6%
(7) Subtotal	-2,842	35.1%	-753	4.1%
INCENTIVES FOR EFFICIENCY, RENEWABLES, AND ALTERNATIVE FUELS				
(8) Energy Efficiency	-570	7.0%	-3,733	20.5%
(9) Renewable Energy & Alternative Fuels	0	0%	-7,912	43.4%
(10) Subtotal	-570	7.0%	-11,645	63.9%
(11) Net Energy Tax Cuts	-8,010	100%	-18,218	100%
(12) Non Energy Tax Cuts	0		-202	
(13) Total Energy and Non-Energy Tax Cuts	0		-18,421	
(14) Tax Increases	0		+4,366	
(15) NET TAX CUTS	-8,010		-14,055	

Source: CRS estimates based on Joint Tax Committee reports.

One way to briefly compare the two measures is to compare revenue losses from the energy tax incentives alone and the percentage distribution by type of incentive as a percent of the net energy tax cuts, in row 11. The net revenue losses over an 11-year time frame from FY2005 to FY2015 were estimated by the Joint Committee on Taxation. The total revenue losses are reported in two ways. First, the absolute dollar value of tax cuts over 11 years are in the odd-numbered columns. Second, the even-numbered columns show the percentage distribution of total revenue losses by type of incentive for each measure.

Table 2 illustrates the major differences between the two energy tax measures, measured in terms of projected aggregate revenue losses. First, the SFC bill is more than twice the size, in terms of net energy tax cuts, as the House bill. Second, most of this difference is accounted for by tax cuts for the electricity industry, energy efficiency and renewable and alternative fuels. The SFC bill provides absolutely and relatively more tax cuts for energy efficiency and alternative fuels. The differences in tax cuts for alternative fuels are particularly striking: $11.6 billion in the SFC bill vs. $0.6 billion in the House bill. The SFC bill also provides more tax incentives for energy efficiency investments than the House bill. The House bill provides much larger tax cuts for the electricity industry, particularly for electricity infrastructure. Thus, in a relative sense, the House bill is tilted more toward fossil fuel production, while the SFC bill's tax cuts are tilted more to the production of alternative and renewable fuels and energy conservation. However, the abolute dollar tax cuts for oil, gas, and coal are also somewhat larger in the SFC bill than in the House bill ($5.8 billion vs. $4.7 billion).

Finally, the FY2006 budget, unveiled February 7 by the Bush Administration, calls for a 10-year energy tax cut of about $6.7 billion, as follows:

- a 15% tax credit for residential solar energy systems to generate electricity or to heat water in homes,
- a deduction for contributions to nuclear decommissioning funds made by unregulated taxpayers,
- a $4,000 tax credit for the purchase of certain hybrid vehicles and a credit of up to $8,000 for fuel cell vehicles,
- a 10% investment tax credit for combined heat and power systems that meet certain specifications for electrical capacity,
- an extension for two years of an existing credit for electricity produced from wind, biomass other than agricultural livestock waste nutrients, and landfill gas. That credit would apply to electricity produced at facilities placed in service before January 1, 2008, Treasury said in the blue book.

LEGISLATION

H.R. 6 (Barton)

Among other provisions, the Energy Policy Act of 2005 would open up the Arctic National Wildlife Refuge (ANWR) to exploration and development, includes a "safe harbor" provision to protect methyl tertiary-butyl ether (MTBE) refiners from product liability suits, would establish a "refinery revitalization" program, and would permit the Federal Energy Regulatory Commission (FERC) to decide on the siting of liquified natural gas (LNG) terminals. Introduced on April 18, 2005. Approved by the House on April 21, 2005 by a vote of 249 to 183.

H.R. 17 (Hayworth)

To amend the Internal Revenue Code of 1986 to allow a credit for residential solar energy property. Introduced January 4, 2005. Referred to House Committee on Ways and Means.

H.R. 36 (King)

To amend the Internal Revenue Code of 1986 to provide for a small agri-biodiesel producer credit and to improve the small ethanol producer credit. Introduced January 4, 2005. Referred to House Committee on Ways and Means.

H.R. 1541 (Thomas)

To amend the Internal Revenue Code of 1986 to enhance energy infrastructure properties in the United States and to encourage the use of certain energy technologies, shorten the depreciation period for natural gas lines and pollution control facilities and modify various exemptions, deductions, and credits, and for other purposes. Introduced on April 11, and approved (with slight modifications) on April 13 by the House Committee on Ways and Means by a vote of 26 to 11.

H.R. 6, 108th Congress (Tauzin)

To promote energy conservation, and research and development, to provide for energy security and diversity in energy supply for the American people and for other purposes. Incorporates H.R. 39, H.R. 238, H.R. 1531 (the tax provisions), and H.R. 1644. The tax title amends the Internal Revenue Code of 1986 to provide incentives for fossil fuel supply (including coal output incentives), facilitate electricity industry restructuring (which is also an energy supply incentive), and reduce fossil fuel demand through enhanced energy efficiency and alternative and renewable fuels supply. Also provides for revenue offsets. Introduced April 7, 2003; referred to several committees. Passed by the House on April 11, 2003. The Senate version was approved July 31, 2003.

FOR ADDITIONAL READING

U.S. Congress. Senate Budget Committee. *Tax Expenditures: Compendium of Background Material on Individual Provisions.* Committee Print. December 2004. 108th Congress, 2nd Sess.

Joint Tax Committee Description of Energy Tax Policy Tax Incentives Act of 2005, Scheduled for Senate Finance Committee Markup June 16, 2005 (JCX-44-05). June 14, 2005.

CRS Report RS21935. *The Black Lung Excise Tax on Coal*, by Salvatore Lazzari.

CRS Report RL30406. *Energy Tax Policy: An Economic Analysis*, by Salvatore Lazzari.

CRS Report RL32042. Energy Tax Incentives in H.R. 6: The Conference Agreement as Compared with the House Bill and Senate Amendment. December 23, 2003, by Salvatore Lazzari.

CRS Report RL32936. Omnibus Energy Legislation, 109th Congress: Assessment of H.R. 6 As Passed by the House, by Mark Holt and Carol Glover.

INDEX

H

I

J

L

T

U